MATHEMATICS

WITH NUMBERS IN COLOUR

BOOK VII

The original Cuisenaire material
described in this book can be
obtained in Great Britain from
the
CUISENAIRE COMPANY LTD.
40 Silver Street, Reading, RG1 2SU

MATHEMATICS
WITH NUMBERS
IN COLOUR

VII ALGEBRA and GEOMETRY

CALEB GATTEGNO

EDUCATIONAL EXPLORERS
READING

First published in Great Britain
in 1962 by Educational Explorers Ltd
40 Silver Street, Reading, RG1 2SU

Second impression 1966
Revised edition 1969

© *C. Gattegno 1962 and 1969*

ISBN: 978-0-87825-351-7

Printed in Great Britain by
Lamport Gilbert Printers Ltd
Reading, Berkshire

Cover design, D. Mervyn Rawlings

CONTENTS

I

SIMULTANEOUS EQUATIONS
ABOUT DIRECTED NUMBERS

Find a pair knowing another pair

1. Let us start with the following situation: we know that an orange rod is equal to a black and a light-green put end-to-end. We also know that a light-green and a pink put end-to-end are equal to a black rod. Can you see which two rods are such that, put end-to-end, they give the length of the orange rod, while the larger of the two has the same length as the smaller put end-to-end with the pink rod?

2. By going through trial and error you can now attempt to find the pair of rods which put end-to-end are equal to the orange rod, *but also such that* the larger one of the pair has the same length as the smaller put end-to-end with:

   (a)   *the red*
   (b)   *the dark-green*
   or (c)   *the tan*

You will get a different pair each time.

3. In No. 2 we kept the orange rod unchanged while we replaced the pink that we started with in No. 1, by the red, the dark-green and the tan in succession. Now let us change the two lengths and consider the following situations.

Find two rods which put end-to-end equal the length of the orange and red put end-to-end, *but also* such that the larger of the pair has the same length as the smaller put end-to-end with:

   (a)   *the red*
   (b)   *the pink*
   (c)   *the dark-green*
   (d)   *the tan*
   (e)   *the orange*

7

4. Repeat what you did in No. 3, but replace the orange and red put end-to-end by any other lengths, say orange and tan, or by two orange and a red put end-to-end, and find which pair of lengths (note this time we do not say rods) will satisfy the two conditions:

(a) that end-to-end they give the length you have chosen;

(b) that the larger one of the pair has the same length as the smaller with any of the following
(a) the red, (b) the pink, (c) the dark-green, (d) the tan, or (e) the orange.

5. Now that you know how to find any of the pairs that satisfy these two conditions, let us try to discover what we actually do in the solution of the problem.

Since we know that "put end-to-end" is translated by $+$, we can write what we did in No. 1 as follows, using initials for the rods: $b + g = o$ (black $+$ green $=$ orange) and $b - g = p$ (black $-$ green $=$ pink). These two *equations* express what we are told. Part of it goes on the left-hand side and part on the right-hand side. Because there are two conditions which hold at the same time, they are called *simultaneous* conditions, leading to *simultaneous equations*, which are usually written one under the other and linked with a curled bracket, as follows:

$$(1) \quad \begin{cases} b+g=o \\ b-g=p \end{cases}$$

the curled bracket holding them together. The two equations express that we have performed certain operations on two lengths and obtained certain results.

In the problems of sections 2 to 4 we changed the length on the right-hand side of one or both of these equations and looked for a pair of lengths to put in the left-hand sides.

This situation could be expressed as follows:

some length$+$some other length$=$some given length

the same length$-$the same other length$=$another smaller given length

8

This part so far translates what we were given. How do we translate the procedure we followed to find the answer?

Formalisation of the solution

Let us go back to the first two equations (1). We can see that the difference between the two given rods, the orange and the pink, is equal to the dark-green or equal to two light-green ones. This is the clue. For the light-green is equal to the smaller of the two lengths we are after. Indeed, in all cases we can find the smaller answer by halving the difference between the two given rods or lengths. We find the second answer by adding the smaller one to the smaller of the given rods.

Here the solution of (1) takes two stages:

$$\frac{o-p}{2}=g \text{ or } \frac{o-p}{2} \text{ equals the light-green,}$$

is the first step, and the second step is

$$\text{pink} + \text{light-green} = \text{black or } p+g=b.$$

Check whether that was your method, and if it was not, see whether you can agree with it.

6. We can re-write our solution

$$g=\frac{o-p}{2} \text{ and } b=p+g$$

by working out

$$p+g=p+\frac{o-p}{2}$$
$$=\frac{2p+o-p}{2}$$
$$=\frac{o+p}{2}$$

9

So the smaller length we are after is half the difference of the two given lengths, while the bigger one is half their sum.

We can look at this problem in another way. The given rod o has the length of the bigger + the smaller answer, whereas the other given rod p has the length of their difference.

Putting the given rods end-to-end we get

$o+p=$(the bigger + the smaller) + (their difference)

$=$the bigger + (the smaller + their difference)

and now the last bracket is nothing else than the bigger again, so that $o+p =$ twice the bigger, or, the bigger equals half the sum of the two given lengths. Having found first the bigger, we can subtract from it the difference (which is equivalent to the smaller given rod) and obtain the other answer.

$$\frac{o+p}{2} - p;$$

which can be worked out as:

$$\frac{o+p-2p}{2}=\frac{o-p}{2}$$

Hence we found the same answers, but in the opposite order. It follows that we *solve* the given equations either by adding them (which will first give the bigger answer) or by subtracting them (which will first give the smaller answer).

We can explain our method better by using letters which are not the initials of colours. Let x and y represent the lengths we want to find, and A and B the given lengths. Then

$$(2) \quad \begin{cases} x+y=A \\ x-y=B \end{cases}$$

We see that by adding we obtain

$$x+y+x-y=A+B \quad \text{or} \quad 2x=A+B$$

and by subtracting

$$x+y-(x-y)=A-B \text{ or } 2y=A-B.$$

So that we have, equivalent to (2),

$$(3) \quad \begin{cases} 2x=A+B \\ 2y=A-B \end{cases}$$

which is also equivalent to:

$$(4) \quad \begin{cases} x=\dfrac{A+B}{2} \\[2ex] y=\dfrac{A-B}{2} \end{cases}$$

This is the required pair (*solution*) and, (4) being equivalent to (2), the succession of writings (2), (3), (4) tells the story of what we did in order to find the required pair (*x*, *y*) from the given pair (*A*, *B*).

A word about algebra

7. Check all your solutions by replacing *in your head* A and B by the lengths you had chosen, and x and y by the pair you want to find.

Always note that though you change the lengths you never change the procedure for obtaining the answer. We shall say that the procedure expresses the *algebra* of the situation. We could think of any number of choices of lengths, but in all cases we use the procedure of either section 5 or section 6 for finding the answers. When we are interested in the procedure rather than in the answers, we say that it is the algebra of the situation we are interested in. The algebra tells us how to do things and, for that reason, we can use letters when we write what we are doing, instead of numbers or instead of initials of rods. The stress is on adding, subtracting, doubling, halving, etc.; in other words on *the operations*.

8. In this chapter we started with rods and made a choice of two, one of which was the result of an addition and the other the result of a subtraction. Then we asked: from this

pair of rods how can we obtain another pair having the required properties? This way of asking the question clearly tells us of the *transformation* of two equations into two others which will show us the change of stress from what is given to what could have been given, but is now unknown.

Go back to No. 1 and see what we did. We started with the black and the green, and noticed two relations between them. Then we considered these two relations and found that we could use them to challenge us to find from them the rods we had before. This can be so only because we can move, step by step, replace these two relations by two others, and again by two others, until we obtain what we are after.

The transformations of the relations we had we called algebra; so algebra deals with the dynamics of these relationships, which are operations here. The signs $+$ and $-$ were at first on the left-hand side in (2) and we find them in (4) on the right-hand side. This means that we have made use of rules of change concerning the operations. The writings themselves are equivalent with respect to these rules.

Let us make these rules more evident.

(a) In (2) we could have written the second equation first.

So the *system* is not affected by the change of order of the equations.

(b) In (2) we could have written what is on the right first, and then what is on the left, so that it would have looked like this:

$$\begin{cases} A & =x+y \\ x-y=B \end{cases} \text{ or } \begin{cases} A=x+y \\ B=x-y \end{cases} \text{ or } \begin{cases} x+y=A \\ B & =x-y \end{cases}$$

Thus the *symmetry* of the sign $=$ can be made use of.

(c) Since addition is *commutative* but subtraction is not, (2) could also be written as

$$\begin{cases} y+x=A \\ x-y=B \end{cases}$$

Combining all these writings we could have quite a large number of ways of presenting (2). Give them all, while you notice carefully whether it is commutativity of addition, symmetry of equality, or indifference of the order of equations that you are using, starting with (2) as the standard form.

A class of equivalence

9. In what we have done so far we have not yet moved from (2). We have only found all equivalent forms with respect to (a), (b), (c) of No. 8. To go further we need a different rule, and this is what we often meet.

Instead of writing

$$x+y=A$$

we know that we can write

$$x=A-y \text{ or } y=A-x$$

Instead of writing

$$x-y=B$$

we can also put

$$x=B+y \text{ or } y=x-B$$

These are: the reversing of additions or subtractions.

Instead of writing

$$x+y=A$$

we can write

$$x+y+z=A+z \text{ or } x+y-t=A-t$$

for any z or t.

These writings express the *class of equivalence* with respect to addition or subtraction of the given relation: every equality belongs to a class of equivalent equalities in which we add to (or subtract from) both sides the same quantity. We are therefore in possession of means that allow us to alter writings while they remain equivalent with respect to those means.

13

For $x=a$ we can write

$x+1=a+1$	$x+2=a+2$	$x+m=a+m$
$x-1=a-1$	$x-2=a-2$	$x-n=a-n$
$2x=2a$	$3x=3a$	$px=pa$
$\dfrac{x}{2}=\dfrac{a}{2}$	$\dfrac{x}{3}=\dfrac{a}{3}$	$\dfrac{x}{q}=\dfrac{a}{q}$

or combining all that:

$$\frac{p}{q}(x+m)=\frac{p}{q}(a+m)$$

is equivalent to

$$x=a,$$

since all that is *done* to x has been done to a and all that is *done* to a has been done to x, and since a and x were, to start with, one and the same thing.

From

$$x=a$$

we can get

$$x-x=a-x \text{ or } 0=a-x$$

just as from

$$a-x=0 \text{ we can get}$$
$$a-x+x=0+x$$

or

$$a=x$$

From

$$x=a \quad \text{and} \quad y=b$$

we can, of course, as above, get

$$x+y=a+b \quad \text{or} \quad x+b=a+y \quad \text{or} \quad x-y=a-b$$

or $\quad x-b=a-y \quad$ or $\quad y-x=b-a \quad$ or $\quad y-a=b-x \ldots$

All this only tells us what we know, but this time we find it all close together in a short page.

10.　If $x+y=A$ and $x-y=B$

we can have in particular, as we had in No. 6:

$$x+y+x-y=A+B$$
and $$x+y-(x-y)=A-B$$

These two writings are equivalent to:

$$2x=A+B \text{ and } 2y=A-B \text{ which is (3)}$$

or

$$x = \frac{A+B}{2} \text{ and } y = \frac{A-B}{2} \text{ which is (4) of page 11.}[1]$$

11. In all this, we never assumed that in the written subtraction (for example $x-n$ or $x-b$ or $x-y$) the first term was bigger than the second. Of course for us to *perform* a subtraction, this is necessary, but to *write* it, it is not required. $3-7$ can be written just as $a-b$ can be. But while $7-3=4$ we cannot say what $3-7$ is equal to in terms of numbers. Still, with the rods it makes sense.

Put the black rod on your table and the white one on top. We know that we need the dark-green to complete the length. With the red instead of the white, we need the yellow instead of the dark-green; with the yellow instead of the red we need the red instead of the yellow; with the black instead of the yellow we need nothing. For the tan instead of the black we shall need to cut off the equivalent of a white one; for the orange, to cut off the equivalent of a light-green.

In writing we shall translate all this in the following manner:

$7-1$	equals	$+6$
$7-2$	,,	$+5$
$7-5$	,,	$+2$
$7-7$	,,	0

---

[1] We found
$$A-B=2y$$
when working with the rods and hence we know that this is correct.
The writing
$$x+y-(x-y)=A-B=2y$$
yields
$$x+y-(x-y)=2y \text{ or } y+y$$
Hence the removal of the bracket makes both the x disappear and the subtracted y become an added y, while the x's cancel out. The same result could have been obtained by comparing
$$x+y+(y-x)=y+y$$
which tells us a new thing: that instead of subtracting a difference $(x-y)$ we can add its opposite $(y-x)$. See No. 13, p. 19.

15

$$7-8 \quad \text{equals} \quad -1$$
$$7-10 \quad \text{,,} \quad -3$$

the + in front of 6, 5, 2 meaning that we need to add the corresponding rod, the − in front of 1 and 3 that we need to cut off something from the rod placed on top of the black. If this is accepted, we can always write any subtraction *and* find an answer to it or perform it. Find the answers to:

5−2	15−7	12−9	14−13	11−12
7−9	8−11	3−6	17−17	19−13
21−27	23−18	29−31	42−72	75−79
66−46	46−66	100−101	343−342	417−673

Can you check whether the following are true?

$$17-19 = -(19-17) \qquad -(32-73) = 73-32$$
$$a-b \ = -(\ b-a\ ) \qquad -(\ m-n\ ) = \ n-m$$

assuming that any number with + in front can also be read without it.

12. It is customary to call numbers preceded by the sign − *negative numbers* and all others *positive*. Zero must be a positive number by this definition. We shall also use the name *vector* when we do not want to say whether we consider a number positive or negative.

That convention will lead us to another. Each rod has two ends, and if we place a rod on a table in front of us we can distinguish these ends by calling one end the left, and the other the right. We shall say that we *add* two rods when we place them end-to-end so that one left end coincides with one right end. If we place one rod on top of another with the common end to the right or to the left, we see that we could talk of them as end-to-end, but instead of a and b we should have, according to the choice, a and $-b$ or $-a$ and b.

So now we can write

$$(+a)+(+b) \atop (+b)+(+a)} \quad (+a)+(-b) \atop (-b)+(+a)} \quad (+b)+(-a) \atop (-a)+(+b)} \quad (-a)+(-b) \atop (-b)+(-a)}$$

as meaning four of the choices in the following figures, in which we choose *a* to be a larger rod than *b*. The rod placed at the bottom is placed first and written first.

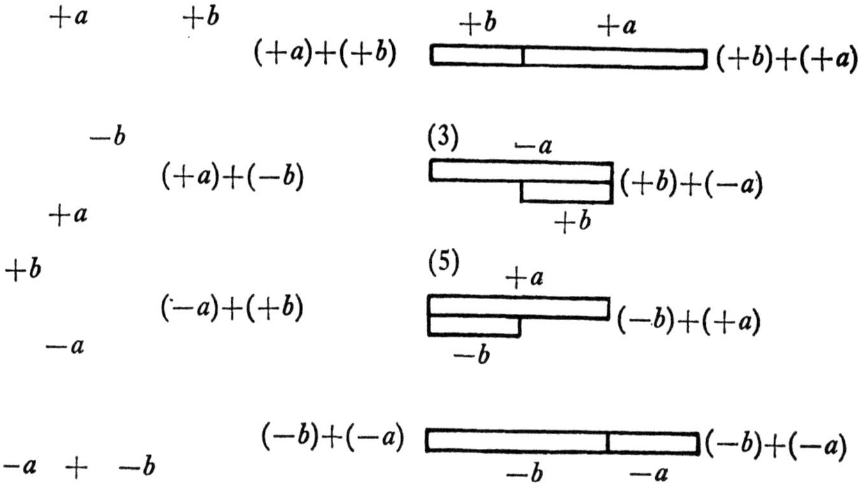

Fig. 1

Let us consider a line in front of us and on it select a point of departure so that the line extends to the right and to the left. This point is called the *origin*. This line, when we work with the rods, is imaginary, but if we draw it here we will see what is meant:

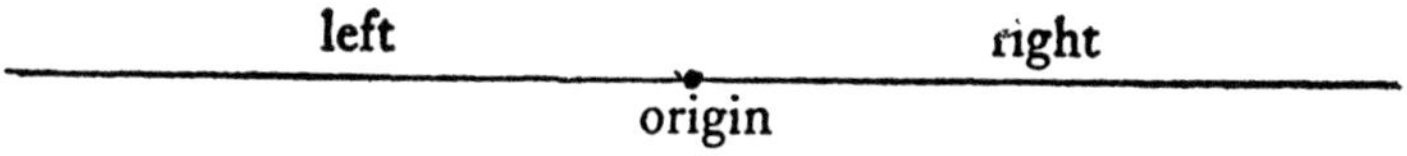

We could take lengths on the line instead of rods. Those on the right we shall mark as +, those on the left as −, as above, and call them, *positive* and *negative* lengths. Putting our lengths end-to-end or on top of each other as we did with the rods we should obtain the following result, the one written at the bottom being placed first:

17

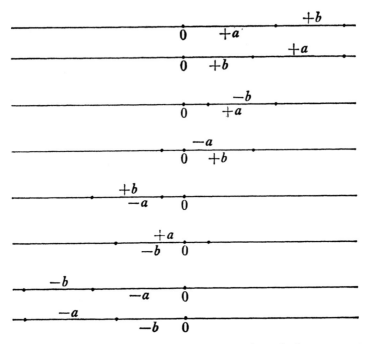

Through this representation we now see that placing one rod on top of another can be regarded as placing them end-to-end but noticing *direction* of the lengths or rods.

The following eight writings correspond to the eight diagrams above:

$+a+b$ or $+b+a$, $+a-b$, $+b-a$, $-a+b$, $-b+a$, $-b-a$ or $-a-b$

In them only the first, the fourth and the fifth seem to be additions while the others look like subtractions. But in the forms above we can look at them as additions of positive and negative numbers or addition of vectors.

The answers are found in the diagram and are:

$$(+a)+(+b)=(a+b)$$
$$(+a)+(-b)=(a-b)$$
$$(+b)+(-a)=(b-a)=-(a-b)$$

18

$$(-a)+(+b)=(b-a)=-(a-b)$$
$$(-b)+(+a)=(a-b)$$
$$(-a)+(-b)=(a+b)$$

These lengths without their signs are called the *absolute values* of the vectors and are written using two vertical lines. Are the following true?

$|a+b|$ or absolute value of $(a+b)$ is equal to
   $|-(a+b)|$

$|a-b|$ or absolute value of $(a-b)$ is equal to
   $|b-a|$

Though we have six writings we only have four different results and two different absolute values.

We can single out the result that

$$(+a)+(-b)$$

in particular, is equal to $(a-b)$ or $(+a)-(+b)$, now using the $-$ sign to mean substraction. We can conclude that to *add a negative number is equivalent to subtracting a positive one* and in algebra we can say that only addition is needed.

What we could not do in arithmetic, because we wanted to count always in the same way, is now possible in all cases. $3-7=-4$ can be used just as easily as $7-3=+4$. Likewise $a-b$ or $b-a$ are as easily written, considered or used.

13. We can now go back to

$$x+y-(x-y)$$

This can be written

$$x+y+(y-x)=x+y+y-x=2y$$

and we find a new justification for the result above.

Generalisation

14. Considering again the simultaneous equations

$$(1) \quad \begin{cases} x+y=A \\ x-y=B \end{cases}$$

if we replace x by $3z$ and y by $2t$ we can find z and t.
The equations will have the following forms:

$$\begin{cases} 3z+2t=A \\ 3z-2t=B \end{cases}$$

and as before we can replace this system by the transformed one

$$\begin{cases} 6z=A+B \\ 4t=A-B \end{cases}$$

by just adding the two equations for the first, and subtracting them for the second. Hence

$$z=\frac{A+B}{6} \qquad t=\frac{A-B}{4}$$

is the solution.

There has been no added difficulty in substituting $3z$ for x and $2t$ for y, nor will there be if we use other numbers instead of 3 and 2, and letters other than z or t.

When A and B are numbers the last results can be calculated and numbers found for the quantities on the left-hand side. This substitution of numbers for the letters, of course, *adds work* and nothing else. In problems, it is often the case that we must find a particular answer; so find the *numerical solution* to the following systems of simultaneous equations:

$$\begin{cases} x+y=11 \\ x-y=\ 3 \end{cases} \qquad \begin{cases} 2z+t=17 \\ 2z-t=\ 3 \end{cases} \qquad \begin{cases} 4u+3v=25 \\ 4u-3v=\ 7 \end{cases}$$

$$\begin{cases} \dfrac{r}{2}+\dfrac{s}{3}=2 \\ \\ \dfrac{r}{2}-\dfrac{s}{3}=0 \end{cases} \qquad \begin{cases} 2\dfrac{m}{3}+4\dfrac{n}{5}=12 \\ \\ 2\dfrac{m}{3}+4\dfrac{n}{5}=4 \end{cases} \qquad \begin{cases} \tfrac{1}{2}p+3q=27 \\ \tfrac{1}{2}p-3q=\ 3 \end{cases}$$

In Book VI Part VIII you can find some problems you could solve using what you have learnt in this chapter. Try them out.

15a. What happens if we do not have the pattern above for our equations—that is, if the letters used in them are no longer preceded by similar numerals? Can we, for example, still solve simultaneous equations of the following type:

$$\begin{cases} 3x+2y=A \\ 4x-2y=B \end{cases}$$

using similar methods?

The answer is obvious because

$$A+B=3x+2y+4x-2y$$

provides already that

$$7x=A+B;$$

hence

$$x=\frac{A+B}{7} \text{ and } 3x=\tfrac{3}{7}\times(A+B)$$

Hence

$$\tfrac{3}{7}x\,(A+B)+2y=A$$

gives $2y$ as $A-\tfrac{3}{7}\times(A+B)$

and y as $\tfrac{1}{2}\times[A-\tfrac{3}{7}\times(A+B)]$.

Hence

$$\begin{cases} 3x+2y=A \\ 4x-2y=B \end{cases}$$

is equivalent to

$$\begin{cases} x=\dfrac{A+B}{7} \\ y=\tfrac{1}{2}\times[A-\tfrac{3}{7}\times(A+B)] \end{cases}$$

21

15b. In the above example we changed only one of the numerals. Can we have a system with four different coefficients[1]? The answer obviously is again 'yes'.

$$\begin{cases} 3x+5y=A \\ 4x-2y=B \end{cases}$$

becomes by a very easy transformation:

$$\begin{cases} 2\times 3x+2\times 5y=2\times A \\ 5\times 4x-2\times 5y=5\times B \end{cases}$$

in which one coefficient on each line equals 10. We are therefore brought back to the case above, which we know how to handle.

15c. Summing up, and using letters as coefficients in order to display the operations only, we can present the algebra of the situation or transformation of the situation so that the separated x and y appear as one of the forms, as follows:

$$\begin{cases} ax+by=A \\ cx+dy=B \end{cases}$$

$$\begin{cases} d\times ax+d\times by=d\times A \\ b\times cx+b\times dy=b\times B \end{cases}$$

$$\begin{cases} d\times ax+b\times dy=d\times A \\ b\times B-b\times dy=b\times cx \end{cases}$$

In this form we are back to what we did in 15b. To give the details, we can see that

$$\begin{cases} d\times ax+b\times B=d\times A+b\times cx \\ cx+dy\quad =B \end{cases}$$

or

$$\begin{cases} (d\times a-b\times c)\times x=d\times A-b\times B \\ cx+dy=B \end{cases}$$

[1]This word is used to describe the factor which is not the yet unknown separated x or y.

22

or

$$\begin{cases} x = \dfrac{d \times A - b \times B}{d \times a - b \times c} \\ cx + dy = B \end{cases}$$

or

$$\begin{cases} x = \dfrac{d \times A - b \times B}{d \times a - b \times c} \\[2em] dy = B - c \times \dfrac{d \times A - b \times B}{d \times a - b \times c} \end{cases}$$

are equivalent forms leading finally to

$$\begin{cases} x = \dfrac{d \times A - b \times B}{d \times a - b \times c} \\[2em] y = \dfrac{c \times A - a \times B}{d \times a - b \times c} \end{cases}$$

II

PERMUTATIONS
AND COMBINATIONS

Permutations

1. Take two different rods and place them end-to-end. In how many ways can you make that arrangement?

If they were a red and a green the arrangement red-green will be considered as being different from the arrangement green-red. They differ by the position of the rods with respect to each other.

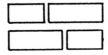

Fig. 2

Now take a third rod, say the white one. In how many different ways can you place these 3 rods end-to-end?

Having found your answer take any other three different rods and find the number of such arrangements end-to-end of these new rods. Do you get the same number again? Is it different from the other? Does the length or the colour of the rods influence your result?

Each such arrangement of rods will be called a *permutation* of the rods. Find the number of permutations of

2 different rods

3 different rods

4 different rods

by making each of the permutations of the rods chosen and keeping them all in front of you.

24

Note whether there are any that you have made twice or more, and only keep one of each of them. Also note whether there are any you have not made. Relate the number of permutations in one group to that of the previous group containing one rod less.

2. Place a red rod in front of you. At how many ends can you put a white rod, say? Make the two permutations thus found.

In how many places in each can you put a third different rod?

Do you think the arrangements made are all different? Why?

Having found all the permutations of these three rods, in how many places in each can you put a fourth different rod?
Can you prove that all the new arrangements are different?
We shall write P_2, P_3, P_4 for the number of permutations of 2 or 3 or 4 different rods.

Is it true that $P_3 = 3P_2$, $P_4 = 4P_3$?

What is P_2 compared to P_1? What is P_4 compared to P_2, and then to P_1?

3. Having found P_3 and P_4 by the method of No. 2, can you without using the rods find the value of

$$P_5$$
$$P_6$$
$$P_7 \quad ?$$

4. Now we can see that, if we know what P_{10} is, we can get P_{11} by just multiplying P_{10} by 11. If you are not sure, make one of the arrangements of 10 different rods and use a pen or pencil to represent an eleventh rod. In how many different places can you insert the pencil?

So with each arrangement of P_{10} we can form 11 new ones containing eleven lengths or: $P_{11} = 11 \times P_{10}$.

Replacing P_{10} by $10 \times P_9$ and so on, and P_1 by 1, can you show that

$$P_{11}=1\times2\times3\times4\times5\times6\times7\times8\times9\times10\times11?$$
Calculate
$$P_1,\ P_2,\ P_3,\ P_4,\ P_5,\ P_6,\ P_7,\ P_8,\ P_9,\ P_{10},\ P_{11},\ P_{12}.$$
The number of permutations of the rods can be written
$$P_K=1\times2\times3\times\ \ldots\ \times K \text{ (where } K \text{ is any integer).}$$
This product is denoted $K!$ and called *factorial K*.

5. To get a better idea of what we have just found, consider ten boys lined up against a wall. In how many different ways could you arrange them?

Or, if twelve people sit around a table, in how many different ways do you think they can place themselves?

To add an exercise that will help you to understand the magnitude of factorials as well as the usefulness of permutations, let us imagine that in order to pass from one permutation to another we take 1 second of time; how long will it take the 12 people round the table to exhaust all possible arrangements? We have to divide P_{12} by 86,400 to find the number of days or by $86,400\times365$ to find the number of years. The best method of working this out is to cancel common factors. We get 56×99 days, which is more than 15 years.

Transpositions and substitutions

6. With the permutations formed with 3 different rods we can make some interesting observations.

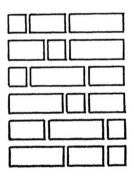

Fig. 3

26

Make your table of permutations of 3 rods. That is, using the actual rods, form your set of 6 different permutations. Call any one of them No. 1 and separate it from the others. If we call the act of interchanging two of the rods, or two groups of rods, *transposition*, what happens to No. 1 if you submit it to 1, 3, 5, 7 . . . transpositions?

What happens if you submit it to 2, 4, 6, 8 . . . transpositions? Can you say after what number of *different* transpositions you come back to No. 1?

The 6 permutations are thus subdivided into 2 sets of 3.

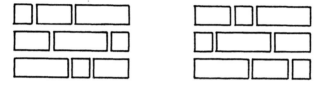

Fig. 4

Can you say which transpositions keep the sets apart and which make you pass from one set to the other?

Start again with No. 1. What must you do to come back to it? If we call the three rods of one permutation *w*, *r*, *g* in that order and we transpose *w* with *r*, *r* with *g*, *g* with *w*, we obtain first *rgw*, then *gwr* and *wrg* again. These three simultaneous transpositions form what is called a *cyclic permutation*.

wrg will give in turn *gwr* and *rgw* and again *wrg*.

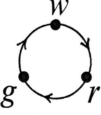

Fig. 5

Any other one of the remaining permutations can be taken in turn and we find that the two sets of three are reproduced

27

by these permutations, without ever passing from one set to the other.

7. Now make your table of permutations of 4 different rods and consider transpositions. Start with any permutation and call it No. 1. What happens to it if you

(1) make an even number of transpositions?
(2) make an odd number of transpositions?
(3) make only cyclic permutations?

Is the table subdivided into two sets like the previous one?

8. Instead of making our tables of permutations we could make one single permutation of a number of rods and by systematic use of transpositions find all permutations of that number of rods. Do it for three rods: w, r, g.

Let us note the original and the final permutations in two lines, putting the rods transposed underneath each other. Thus

$\begin{Bmatrix} w\ r\ g \\ r\ w\ g \end{Bmatrix}$ tells us that w and r have been transposed, while g remained unchanged.

$\begin{Bmatrix} w\ r\ g \\ g\ w\ r \end{Bmatrix}$ tells us that we have transposed first w and r and then r and g.

We shall use the word *substitution* for the passage from one line to the next or the transformation of one permutation into another.

If we now consider two such transformations one after the other, starting with $w\ r\ g$,

$$\begin{Bmatrix} w\ r\ g \\ r\ g\ w \end{Bmatrix} \quad \text{and} \quad \begin{Bmatrix} r\ g\ w \\ r\ w\ g \end{Bmatrix}$$

the second tells us that we have only transposed w and g, so the result of combining the two transformations is given by

$$\begin{Bmatrix} w\ r\ g \\ r\ w\ g \end{Bmatrix}$$

which says that the transposition of w and r could have been obtained (as we already experienced in our trials of No. 6) by transposing w and r, then r and g, then g and w, and then w and r.

If we write

$$\left\{ \begin{matrix} w\ r\ g \\ r\ g\ w \end{matrix} \right\} \ \cdot \ \left\{ \begin{matrix} r\ g\ w \\ r\ w\ g \end{matrix} \right\} \ = \ \left\{ \begin{matrix} w\ r\ g \\ r\ w\ g \end{matrix} \right\}$$

and call it the *product* of two substitutions, we see that the result of two substitutions following each other is a substitution formed by using the first and the last and dropping the middle term common to both (as we did with, for example, $\frac{4}{7} \times \frac{7}{6} = \frac{4}{6}$). We must notice that if we exchange the order of the substitutions in the relation above, we change the meaning of it all and cannot expect to find the same result.

For example, in

$$\left\{ \begin{matrix} r\ g\ w \\ r\ w\ g \end{matrix} \right\} \ \cdot \ \left\{ \begin{matrix} w\ r\ g \\ r\ g\ w \end{matrix} \right\} \ = \ \left\{ \begin{matrix} r\ g\ w \\ g\ r\ w \end{matrix} \right\}$$

what is shown in the notation can be read as follows:

> The first substitution has kept r while transposing g and w.
>
> The second is a cyclic permutation made up of the transpositions of r for w, g for r, and w for g.
>
> The final substitution is obtained by combining the first two as follows:
>
>> r corresponds in the first to r, but in the second to g, so finally r has been changed into g;
>>
>> g in the first corresponds to w, which in the second is replaced by r; thus g goes finally into r;
>>
>> The last shows that as w was changed first into g, and then g changed into w, w will correspond to itself.

All these correspondences appear in the last substitution.

Since with 4 rods there are more permutations, more could be found if we repeated such trials with the permutation *w r g p* and considered transpositions and wrote the initial and final permutations as a substitution in a bracket, as above.

9. The important things we have learned in the study above are

(a) that substitutions can be combined and yield substitutions;

(b) that the product of substitutions is not commutative;

(c) that the algebra of permutations is another example of what we said in Part I, No. 7: that algebra is concerned with what we do rather than with the results found. Substitutions and transpositions are actions and we discovered that these actions follow rules; we found one or two of these. We then saw that these rules could equally well apply to permutations of 4 elements. Now, we could ask: could they apply to any number of elements? The answer is yes, but we must leave this for later.

Combinations

10. If we have 7 *different* rods, we could ask ourselves: in how many ways could we choose 2 or 3 or 5 of them?

Let us start with two different rods: *w* and *r*.

We could choose *w*, or *r*, or *w* and *r*. So for two elements we can have 2 choices of 1 and only one choice of 2.

If we had three different rods *w*, *r*, and *g*, we could choose *w*, or *r*, or *g*, or *w* and *r*, or *w* and *g*, or *r* and *g*, or *w* and *r* and *g*. Let us call *combination* any of the groups we can form by taking so many rods out of the given group. For instance we can form 3 combinations if we are given 2 elements and 7 if we are given 3. But as these combinations contain different numbers of elements, so we shall need a notation with two suffixes, one telling the number of the given elements and one telling us what is the number of elements we choose. Here we shall use

$$_2C_3 \quad \text{or} \quad _7C_{12}$$

to tell that we start with 3 or with 12 and find the number of combinations we can make with 2 elements in each or 7 elements in each. We found above that

$$\begin{aligned}
_1C_2 &= 2 & _2C_2 &= 1 \\
_1C_3 &= 3 & _2C_3 &= 3 & _3C_3 &= 1
\end{aligned}$$

Find with your rods the values of

$$\begin{array}{cccccc}
_1C_4 & _2C_4 & _3C_4 & _4C_4 \\
_1C_5 & _2C_5 & _3C_5 & _4C_5 & _5C_5 \\
_1C_6 & _2C_6 & _3C_6 & _4C_6 & _5C_6 & _6C_6
\end{array}$$

11. Any number can be subdivided into two complementary numbers

$$n = p + (n - p) \qquad p < n$$

So if we start with 5 rods and we form all possible pairs with them, we find that to each pair there corresponds a triplet and conversely. So there are as many combinations of 2 as there are of 3 so that $_2C_5 = _3C_5$. Is this in agreement with what you found?

If you had 7 elements to start with, the complementary numbers are 1 and 6, 2 and 5, 3 and 4. So we should have

$$_1C_7 = {_6C_7} \qquad _2C_7 = {_5C_7} \qquad _3C_7 = {_4C_7}$$

Check this by finding the values of all these expressions.

If you had ten different rods and were to give the equalities of numbers of combinations resulting from the awareness that once you choose a few of the rods, the remaining rods can also be considered as a choice, which would you write?

12. We found in No. 10 by actual counting what a few of these numbers were. The result of No. 11 tells us that we need to count only half the numbers since the number of combinations of two complementary numbers are equal.

It is clear that if we want to find the number of combinations of 3 rods taken from 7 rods, we shall need to know the number of combinations of 7 rods 2 by 2, for, out of the 7 given rods, if we choose 3, these three are made of any two to which a third is added. So, there will be as many choices of 3 as there are for each choice of 2, a choice of 1 among the 5 left, except that this time the same combination may have been taken more than once.

In order to simplify the calculations let us go back to groups of 3, 4, 5, 6 rods before we consider the case of 7.

For three, we already know

$$_1C_3 = 3 = {_2C_3} \qquad _3C_3 = 1.$$

For four $\quad _1C_4 = 4 = {_3C_4}$, and $_2C_4 = \frac{3}{2} \times {_1C_4}$;

since for each choice of 1 there are 3 possible choices of another among the remaining 3, and each pair will have been taken twice. So

$$_2C_4 = 3 \times 2 = 6.$$

For five, $\quad _1C_5 = 5 = {_4C_5}$ and $_2C_5 = {_3C_5} = \frac{4}{2} \times {_1C_5}$

since for each choice of 1 there are 4 possible choices of another among the remaining 4 and each pair will have been taken twice. So

$$_2C_5 = {_3C_5} = \frac{4}{2} \times 5 = 10$$

For six $\quad _1C_6 = 6 = {_5C_6} \qquad _2C_6 = {_4C_6} = \frac{5}{2} \times {_1C_6}$

since, as before, the pairs are taken twice and there are 5 choices left of another rod to form a pair. So

$$_2C_6 = {_4C_6} = 5 \times 3 = 15$$

$_3C_6$ is calculated like this: since we have $_2C_6$ pairs and for each pair 4 rods left from which we can make four choices of one, a number of triplets will not be distinct; each triplet will have been taken 3 times, since if we have a triplet, red, green, black, this can be the outcome of adding any one to a remaining pair, red to green and black, or green to red and black, or black to green and red. So we must divide by 3 to have the exact number of combinations.

$$_3C_6 = \frac{4}{3} \times {_2C_6} = 4 \times 5 = 20$$

Let us put all these numbers in a Table

No. of rods	No. of combinations containing each					
	1 or	2 or	3 or	4 or	5 or	6 elements
1	1					
2	2	1				
3	3	3	1			
4	4	6	4	1		
5	5	10	10	5	1	
6	6	15	20	15	6	1
etc.						

This table (or Pascal's Triangle) shows remarkable features. Try to find in the successive columns some link between the number and its successor or predecessor.

For that write the successive series like this

1, 2, 3, 4, 5, 6 . . .

1, 3, 6, 10, 15 . . .

1, 4, 10, 20 . . .

and see whether the first missing number, when you get it, is the correct one by working out the last line of the triangle. We already know why some numbers in the triangle are equal.

Is it true that each number in the triangle is equal to the one above plus the one on the left of that one? For this to be correct we need to introduce on the left a column made of ones and assume that a blank above a number is to be replaced by a zero.

We can, using this observation, re-write Pascal's triangle and extend it to any line we want. Do it up to and including the 13th line. The observations above are written

$$_pC_m = {}_pC_{m-1} + {}_{p-1}C_{m-1}$$

where p is the number of the column and m that of the line.

Computation of permutations and combinations

13. We already know that

$$_2C_4 = \tfrac{3}{2}\times {}_1C_4, \quad {}_2C_5 = \tfrac{4}{2}\times {}_1C_5 \quad \text{and} \quad {}_1C_4 = 4, \qquad {}_1C_5 = 5$$

So
$$_2C_4 = \frac{3\times 4}{2} \qquad\qquad {}_2C_5 = \frac{4\times 5}{2}$$

or looking at all the numbers in Pascal's triangle we find that any one can be obtained from the preceding one on the same row by a multiplication and a division, for example

$$\begin{array}{ccccccc} 1 & 6 & 15 & 20 & 15 & 6 & 1 \end{array}$$

$$\frac{1\times 6}{1}=6 \quad \frac{6\times 5}{2}=15 \quad \frac{15\times 4}{3}=20 \quad \frac{20\times 3}{4}=15 \quad \frac{15\times 2}{5}=6$$

or

$$_2C_6={}_1C_6\times\tfrac{5}{2}, \quad {}_3C_6={}_2C_6\times\tfrac{4}{3}, \quad {}_4C_6={}_3C_6\times\tfrac{3}{4}, \quad {}_5C_6={}_4C_6\times\tfrac{2}{5},$$
$$_6C_6={}_5C_6\times\tfrac{1}{6}$$

since

$$_1C_6=6 \text{ then } {}_2C_6=\frac{6\times 5}{2}; \ {}_3C_6=\frac{6\times 5\times 4}{2\times 3}; \ {}_4C_6=\frac{6\times 5\times 4\times 3}{2\times 3\times 4};$$

$$_5C_6=\frac{6\times 5\times 4\times 3\times 2}{2\times 3\times 4\times 5}; \ {}_6C_6=\frac{6\times 5\times 4\times 3\times 2\times 1}{2\times 3\times 4\times 5\times 6}$$

Find similarly the values in a few of the successive lines of the triangle as fractions of products.

Let us observe that the denominators are always equal to the factorial of the first suffix. All numerators start with the second suffix and contain as many factors as there are units in the first suffix: 1 for $_1C_p$, 2 for $_2C_p$, ... 5 for $_5C_p$ etc.

So we can say that the denominator of $_pC_m$ is p! The numerator contains the product of m with consecutive numbers smaller than m and we must stop when p of them have been taken:

for 1 it will be equal to m

" 2   " $m \times (m-1)$

" 3   " $m \times (m-1) \times (m-2)$

" 4   " $m \times (m-1) \times (m-2) \times (m-3)$

and for p " $m \times (m-1) \times (m-2) \times \ldots (m-p+1)$

since $m-3+1=m-2$ $m-4+1=m-3$
are the last factors in the 3rd and 4th line.

So we can say that:

$$_pC_m = \frac{m(m-1)\,(m-2)\,\ldots\,(m-p+1)}{p!}$$

Check this formula for all the numbers you found in your triangle. Note that this fraction is a whole number in every case. We must conclude that: The product of p consecutive numbers is always divisible by factorial p.

14. To give an idea of the growth of factorials the following table will be useful.

$1! = 1$

$2! = 2$

$3! = 6$

$4! = 24$

$5! = 120$

$6! = 720$

$7! = 5,040$

$8! = 40,320$

$9! = 362,880$

$10! = 3,628,800$

$11! = 39,916,800$

$12! = 479,001,600$

$13! = 6,227,020,800$

$14! = 87,178,291,200$

$15! = 1,307,674,368,000$

$16! = 20,922,789,888,000.$

Compare factorials and powers of a given number. For what value of n will the factorial of n be greater than 2^n, 3^n, ... 10^n? For example for $n=4$ $n!=24$ while $2^4=16$ and $3^4=81$. Is $n!$ bigger or smaller than 10^n for $n=20$?

15. In the next chapter we shall meet applications of combinations (see Part III No. 5) as choices of elements in a given set. But there are many more uses for them and in your future studies you will find your present knowledge most helpful.

Here let us consider for example how many different groups of 4 players can be formed in a bridge club which has 20 members? This is a straightforward application of the formula of No. 13, with $p=4$ and $m=20$:

$$_4C_{20}=\frac{20\times19\times18\times17}{1\times2\times3\times4}=4845$$

so that the club members could have 4,845 games to play before the same 4 people would have to come together.

There are 36 children in one class and they go into their class 2 by 2. How many different pairs can you form?

If in a school the dancing club has 16 boys and 16 girls, how many dancing couples can you make excluding those made of 2 boys or 2 girls? (Here you will have to operate upon results obtained when using arithmetical operations on combinations.)

III

SETS AND SUBSETS

ALGEBRA OF SETS

Sets and elements

1. Take your rods and place them on the table in front of you. They form a *set*. If you remove a few or add some more they always form a set. So the word set applies to a collection of objects, whatever their number.

Think of various sets. Here are a few examples. Your hairs form a set; the hands of all the pupils in your school, the words on this page or in this book, the letters used to compose them, the grains of sand on a beach, and the drops of rain in a shower. All these are sets.

You see that every time you think of sets you also think of what objects enter into it. These are called the *elements* of the set. Your rods are the elements of the set of rods in front of you.

2. Start with the set in front of you and remove one rod only. Have you still got a set? Remove another one and another one and another one . . . . Have you in every case still got a set? It is obvious that if you go on doing that, you will reach a stage at which first one rod will be left and then none. It seems absurd to call one rod a set. But we shall still do so, because it is convenient *not* to insist that a set must have more than one element.

When you think of the most precious stones, you do not know in advance whether there are one or more. So the set of most precious stones may consist of just one stone.

Let us also note that the set made of one element is not identical with that element, for if we said "Phileas Habakuk is the only man who can live on glass", we consider the set of men who live on glass and find that only P.H. satisfies that

37

condition. P.H. fills the condition and belongs to the set which this time reduces to him. If you find this too difficult, leave it aside and read on.

The null set

3. What is more, we shall also consider *null sets*. These are the sets with no element. For instance, every time you put two contradictory conditions together you find a null set.

All the weeks of four Thursdays

All months of seven weeks

All nights that are days

All dead that are alive

All completely bald heads that are covered with natural hair
. . . etc.

Form sets that are null. Give examples of your own showing that there are occasions when words lead to the consideration of null sets.

In fact, if I do not know how many rods I have in front of me and I do not look at them while some one removes the rods one by one, I shall answer the question "Have you still got a set?" by "yes", even when he removes the last rod. So null sets arise naturally on various occasions and we can get used to them now.[1]

Relationships between sets

4. In your set of rods you can take handfuls. Do it several times, each time putting the rods back. Most likely each choice of your handfuls will be a different one. It is clear that your handful consists of rods of your initial set. It is a part of it. It is a set *contained* in another. We shall say it is a *subset* of the given set.

[1]In earlier books in this series we used the word *class* every time we started with an *attribute*. *Set* and *class* can replace each other in some propositions but they can be very distinct notions. A *class* extends to all possible objects having the same attribute in common and is indefinite, while a *set* is definite because it is the aggregate of the elements that go to form it. For example, all the possible (colour) reds form a class, while all red cars form a set. When we speak of classes we use the word *empty* where *null* is used with sets.

Take two successive handfuls, this time noting which rods are in each. If the two subsets have no rod in common[1] we shall say they are *disjoint*. For instance, consider one handful and what remains of the set in front of you. They are disjoint. Together they form the initial set and for that reason they are called two *complementary* subsets.

Of course we could have more than two disjoint subsets in a given set, or even two disjoint subsets which, with a third subset, also disjoint to each, form the initial set.

The division of a set into disjoint subsets which when taken together, form the initial set, is called a *partition* of the set of m distinct elements.

Form several distinct partitions of your set of rods.

5. In Part II we introduced combinations as choices of elements in a given set and we calculated their number. If now you start with a set of 1 or 2 or 3 or 4 or . . . *different* rods and look for the number of possible choices you can make or the number of distinct *subsets* in those sets you will find the same numbers as in Part II. That is, $_pC_m$ will be the number of subsets of p elements that you can form out of a set of m distinct elements.

Find the number of subsets in a set formed of

5 distinct elements

7 distinct elements,   by actually forming the subsets.

6. We now see how the number of subsets of a given set can be found. Among the subsets we must include two special ones; the null set or choice of no rod, and the whole set or choice of all the rods. The last two subsets are called *improper* subsets and the others *proper*. If we do not want to exclude the improper subsets, we shall only talk of the subsets of a given set.

---

[1] If the rods of a set can be distinguished by colour or length, it is easy to see whether they belong to a set or not. We shall assume that even when they have the same colour or size, they have some mark that distinguishes any two of them and give a meaning to the expression: no rod in common.

For a set formed of 6 distinct elements we can form

6 subsets of one element

15 subsets of two elements

20 subsets of three elements

15 subsets of four elements

6 subsets of five elements

This makes 62 proper subsets, and adding the 2 improper ones we have altogether 64 subsets. Add all the numbers in each of the lines of Pascal's triangle. You will find something remarkable. Since $64=2^6$, can you express each of your results as a power of 2? Which?

Is it true that the number of subsets of a set of m elements is equal to 2^m?

Check it on all your results.

Inclusion

7. If we know that a set S_1 is contained in a set S_2 we shall write this as

$$S_1 \subset S_2$$

which is read either as "S_1 is contained in S_2" or "S_2 contains S_1". The last expression is also written as

$$S_2 \supset S_1$$

The two writings are equivalent.

$\subset$ and $\supset$ are the signs for the relationship of *inclusion*.

Practice it using your handfuls of rods. Take a set and a handful in it. Call the first S and the second S' and write down their relationship of inclusion. To test whether you are right, take a rod belonging to S'; does it belong also to S? If it does for every rod of S', then $S' \subset S$.

Note that this time you can separate S' from S in your mind without actually taking the rods of S' away; for if you took the rods away you would see S' and *what is left* of S, and not S.

Take a rod belonging to S; does it belong to S'?

Now take two sets at random; do you still think there is a relationship of inclusion between them?

Here are a few examples:

Compare for inclusion the following pairs of sets.

(a) The inhabitants of London and those of England.
     ,,   ,,   ,,   ,,   ,,   Scotland.
     ,,   ,,   ,,   ,,   ,,   Great Britain.

(b) Your hairs and those of your parents.

(c) The words on this page and those in all Bibles.
     ,,   ,,   ,,   ,,   all those printed since 1900.
     ,,   ,,   ,,   ,,   all the characters of this book.

You must always first consider whether the elements of the two sets are *comparable* if you want to use the relationship of belonging. For instance, are words characters? are characters words? Then you must say: if I call the two sets S and S', and if a is an element of S, does it also belong to S'? and conversely? If both answers are yes, then you can say $S = S'$. The equality of sets thus results from their identity. It also results from the two relations:

$$S \supset S' \quad \text{and} \quad S \subset S'$$

holding at the same time.

For instance the set S of the inhabitants of a country and the set formed by taking together the inhabitants of towns, T, and those of villages, V, farms, F, etc. are identical. For, if a belongs to S it either belongs to T or to V or to F, etc. If b belongs to T, because $T \subset S$ then b belongs to S, etc. So we have proved that any element of any one of the sets T, V, or F belongs to S and that any element of S is an element of T or V or F. This ensures equality. When a set is contained in another, we shall say it is *smaller* than the other or that the other is *bigger* than the first.

We met in previous books the notation $<$ and $\leqslant$ for *inequality* of numbers. Here we met the notation for *inclusion* of sets $\subset$. It is clear that these two notions are very close to each

41

other. What we said of inequality of numbers can be expressed as inclusions of sets if we replace the numbers by the sets of their units. The use of the words smaller and bigger between sets show the opposite trend; that is of expressing inclusion as a relation of order.

Equivalence of sets

8. In Book V we studied numerical sets and introduced the notion of *equivalence* of two sets S_1 and S_2. If with each element of S_1 we can associate an element of S_2, and with each element of S_2 we can associate an element of S_1, then S_1 and S_2 are said to be equivalent.

We have already met the properties of the equivalence relation in several places in our books.

Prove, from the definition above, that if we denote equivalence of sets by $\sim$, then

(i) $S \sim S$

(ii) If $S_1 \sim S_2$ then $S_2 \sim S_1$

(iii) If $S_1 \sim S_2$ and $S_2 \sim S_3$ then $S_1 \sim S_3$

The first property of the relation is called *symmetry*, while the second is called *reflexivity* and the third *transitivity*. You can try to prove that equality (represented by the notation $=$) has these three properties.

We said in Book V that a set is infinite if it is such that it can be put into a *one—one correspondence* with one of its proper subsets; this means that the two sets are equivalent. We gave many examples. Let us recall the set of whole numbers and the set of even numbers

$$
\begin{array}{ccccccc}
1 & 2 & 3 & 4 & 5 & \ldots & n & \ldots \\
\updownarrow & \updownarrow & \updownarrow & \updownarrow & \updownarrow & & \updownarrow & \\
2, & 2\times2, & 2\times3, & 2\times4, & 2\times5, & \ldots & 2\times n & \ldots
\end{array}
$$

Operations on sets

9. In order to be able to work with sets, we shall introduce, in addition to the notions of equality, equivalence, inclusion,

one—one correspondence, etc. two operations on sets which will be called *intersection* and *union*.

Take two sets of rods; three things may happen:

(a) either they have no rod in common, and we say they are disjoint, or

(b) they have all their rods in common, and we say they are identical or equal, or

(c) they have some rods in common, and we say that they meet or intersect or have a common part.

The *intersection* of two sets of rods S_1 and S_2 is the set of the rods they have in common; it is written $S_1 \cap S_2$.

We can write all the elements of a set of rods in curly brackets, writing $3r$ to denote three red rods, etc.

If we take

$$S_1 = \{y, 3r, 2b, 4p, o, B\}$$
$$\text{and} \quad S_2 = \{2r, 3y, p, 2o, g, 4b\}$$

then the set of rods that belong at the same time to S_1 and S_2 is the intersection

$$S_1 \cap S_2 = \{y, 2r, 2b, p, o\}$$

[Here we have to agree that rods of the same colour or the same length are not to be considered as distinct.]

Repeat this type of exercise several times until you feel that you know what is meant by intersection.

10.   Consider now $S \cap S'$, this time in order to find the properties of the operation which associates a set (the intersection) with two given sets.

Is the operation $\cap$ such that

$$S \cap S' = S' \cap S?$$

We know that if it is, we can call $\cap$ a commutative operation.

Is

$$S \cap (S' \cap S'') = (S \cap S') \cap S''?$$

In other words, is the operation associative?

Does
$$S_1 \cap S_2 = S_1$$
mean that S_1 is contained in S_2?

What would $S_1 \cap S_2 = S_2$ mean?

Can you express the last two relations using the notion of inclusion and the signs $\subset$ and $\supset$?

Let $S_1, S_2, S_3 \ldots S_{10}$ be the following sets of rods:

S_1: one white rod

S_2: one white and one red

S_3: one white, one red and one light-green

S_4: one white, one red, one light-green, one crimson

$S_5, S_6 \ldots S_9$ constructed similarly up to

S_{10}: one of each colour.

Using the three signs $\subset$, $\supset$, $\cap$, write down all the possible relations between these sets $S_1, S_2 \ldots S_{10}$.

The notation for a null set is ø. Two disjoint sets have a null intersection; are any of the following writings true?

$$S_3 \cap S_7 = \text{ø} \quad S_5 \cap S_9 = \text{ø} \quad S_{10} \cap S_1 = \text{ø?}$$

11. The other operation, which we shall denote by $\cup$, is defined like this; with each pair of sets S_1 and S_2 we shall associate a set $S_1 \cup S_2$ called the *union* of S_1 and S_2, of which the following example gives an idea:

$$S_1 = \{w, 5r, 2y, 5p, 3b, 2o\}$$
$$S_2 = \{3w, 7g, p, 2y, b, B, o\}$$
$$S_1 \cup S_2 = \{3w, 5r, 7g, 5p, 2y, 3b, B, 2o\}$$

The number of rods of any colour in $S_1 \cup S_2$ is the larger number of rods of that colour contained in S_1 or S_2.

[Here we have to agree that rods of the same colour or the same length are not to be considered as distinct.]

As above, take several pairs of handfuls of rods and form their union.

May we only consider two sets? Try to form the union of three handfuls of rods, writing them down as above.

Is the operation ∪ such that

$$S_1 \cup S_2 = S_2 \cup S_1?$$

We know that if it is, we can call ∪ a commutative operation.

Is

$$S_1 \cup (S_2 \cup S_3) = (S_1 \cup S_2) \cup S_3?$$

In other words, is the operation associative?

Interpret in terms of inclusion the following writings

$$S_1 \cup S_2 = S_1$$
$$S_1 \cup S_2 = S_2$$

If you have difficulties, use your rods.

Analogy between operations on sets and on products

12. Let us examine the way in which we form the intersection of two sets and the H.C.F. of two composite numbers. When two sets are given, their elements are not structured in any way; they are just there. When a number is decomposed into its prime factors, the number is *their* product; though we can change the order of the factors we must think of them as linked by multiplication.

Using the rods, make a *tower* formed of two blacks, one yellow, three greens, and two reds; and another formed of one black, three yellows, two greens, and four reds. (If we wish to know which number each tower represents we can measure each rod with the white one and write

$$N_1 = 7^2 \times 5 \times 3^3 \times 2^2 = 26{,}460 \qquad N_2 = 7 \times 5^3 \times 3^2 \times 2^4 = 126{,}000)$$

Let S_1 be the set of rods which make up the first tower but considered as lying in a heap on the table. Similarly S_2 is the set of rods corresponding to the second tower.

If we now form the successive steps in the two ways in which we used our rods, we can see that we can say

considering N_1 and N_2 r is a common *factor* of N_1 and N_2	considering S_1 and S_2 r is a common *element* of S_1 and S_2
g ,,	g ,,
r^2 ,,	r and r are ,, s ,,
y ,,	y is ,,
$r \times g$,,	r and g are ,, s
b ,,	b is ,,
g^2 ,,	g and g are ,, s
$r \times y$,,	r and y ,, s
$r^2 \times g$,,	r and r and g ,, s
$r \times b$,,	r and b ,, s
$r^2 \times y$,,	r and r and y ,, s
$r^2 \times b$,,	r and r and b ,, s
$r \times g \times y$,,	r and g and y ,, s
$r^2 \times g \times b$,,	r and r and g and b ,, s
$r^2 \times g^2 \times y$,,	r and r and g and g and y ,, s
$r^2 \times g^2 \times b$,,	r and r and g and g and b ,, s
$r^2 \times g^2 \times y \times b$,,	r and r and g and g and y and b ,, s

We can see that the numerical value of the factors increases and that the towers are formed first of one storey, then of two, then of three, etc., and there may be several towers of each height. But there is only one tower which is the *highest*; this is called the *Highest Common Factor* of N_1 and N_2 or H.C.F. of N_1, N_2 which we wrote already

$$(N_1, N_2) = r^2 \times g^2 \times y \times b$$

or in figures

$$2^2 \times 3^2 \times 5 \times 7 = 1,260.$$

We can also see that the subsets formed of the rods which are common to S_1 and S_2 may contain one, or two or more elements, there being several subsets of one, several of two, etc., but that there is only one subset which is the *most extended* and this is the one we call the intersection of S_1 and S_2 and denote by $S_1 \cap S_2$.

The table above shows that the analogy of intersection of two sets and H.C.F. of two numbers is complete. Prove to yourself that it is also true if you take more than two sets and numbers. The intersection contains all the subsets that are common to two sets, and is therefore the largest subset common to them. (Sometimes one says *maximal* instead of largest.) The H.C.F. is divisible by all other factors common to two numbers; it too is maximal. We, of course, say that if a tower is made of the rods of another tower and of a few more the smaller is *contained* in it, and the rods are thus very helpful to bring out the analogy.

We could easily show that the analogy between L.C.M. and *union* is also complete. We would form towers that *contain* those of N_1 and N_2 and look for the smallest tower having this property; and we would form sets of which S_1 *and* S_2 are subsets, and find the smallest such set.

Do it yourself using, to begin with, towers and sets with three or four rods each in order to avoid the difficulty of building tall towers. Make a table similar to the one above and note that now you will reduce the tower step by step as you remove rods in it, without changing the property that it contains N_1 and N_2 at every step. You will see that the L.C.M. and the union are *minimal*, as contrasted with the H.C.F. and the intersection, which are maximal.

13. In your future studies you will often come across the two operations of intersection and of union. Go back to numerical sets and using the notations of Book V find the answers to

$$(E) \quad \cup \quad (O)$$
$$(E) \quad \cap \quad (O)$$
$$(I) \quad \cap \quad (E)$$
$$(I) \quad \cup \quad (E) \quad \cup \quad (O)$$
$$(I) \quad \cup \quad [(E) \quad \cap \quad (O)]$$

where (I) is the set of integers, (E) the set of even numbers and (O) the set of odd numbers.

IV

ARITHMETIC PROGRESSIONS
AND GEOMETRIC PROGRESSIONS

Arithmetic progressions

1. From the start of our work with the rods, we saw that staircases could be made, and we used them to find out properties of numbers. Thus using one rod of each colour we formed the series

$$1, 2, 3, 4, \ldots 10.$$

From it we drew the staircases

$$1, 3, 5, 7, 9$$

of the odd numbers, and

$$2, 4, 6, 8, 10$$

of the even numbers.

But we could also form, starting with any rod and always using the same height for the *common difference*, staircases that help us to count in twos, threes, fours, etc., starting at any point in the sequence of integers.

All these staircases display one and the same property, which we are going to study now and which we shall call *arithmetic progression*.

2. Take a number of rods and form a rectangle by putting any number of them side by side as in (a) below. Then choose a large number of rods of one colour but different from *r* and place them side by side as in figure (b) end to end with all but one of the rods of (a). Then, still using the same rods, place another row as in figure (c) end to end with all but one of the rods on the second line of (b) and do that until you reach a figure like (d) ending with one rod only on the last row.

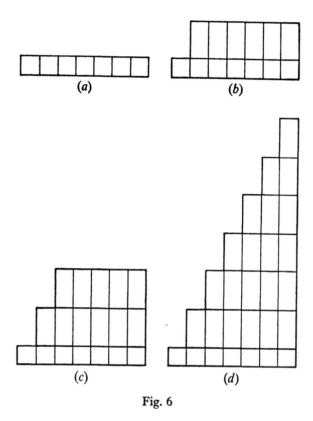

Fig. 6

It is a staircase and we can calculate the height of any level from the ground level represented by the corresponding horizontal line in (d).

Do it with your choice of rods. When you have found the heights in cm., use (instead of figures) the initials of the name of the colours you have chosen and write down the heights of the levels like this:

$$r, r+g, r+2g, r+3g, r+4g \ldots$$

in which red and green rods were chosen.

3. Instead of the initials of the colours we can use another way of writing that can be understood from figure (e). The heights are denoted by h with *suffixes* 0, 1, 2, . . . to show

49

which level is considered. Let H denote the height of the common difference. Thus h_0 represents the bottom step, $h_1=h_0+H$, $h_2=h_0+2H$, etc.

h_0 is called the *first term*

h_n the *general term*.

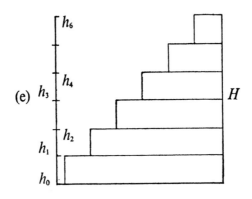

Fig. 7

Prove step by step that

(1) $h_n=h_0+nH$

In this formula we see that there are four quantities which can be altered: either the common difference, or the first term, or the number of steps, or the general term. But if three of these quantities are fixed, the fourth is also fixed because of that. Check whether the following formulae are equivalent to (1).

(2) $nH = h_n-h_0$

(3) $H = \dfrac{h_n-h_0}{n}$

(4) $n = \dfrac{h_n-h_0}{H}$

(5) $h_0 = h_n-nH$

50

4. If instead of starting from the ground level we started from any other level and went up or down a certain number of steps, we would obtain relations like the following

$$h_7 - h_3 = 4H$$
$$h_9 - h_2 = 7H$$

Check them and write some other ones of your choice by actually going up or down your staircase.

Is the following formula correct?

(6) $h_p - h_q = (p - q) H$

What happens if $q = 0$? Have we already met that result?

5. Formula (1), or its various equivalent forms (2) to (5), is one that can give us any one of the 4 *variables* n, H, h_0, h_n which appear in it.

(a) For example, if we write

$$1, 7, 13, 19 \ldots$$

we see that $h_0 = 1$ $H = 6$ and we could ask: find the term whose suffix is 27. This will be given by formula (1) in which we replace h_0 by 1, H by 6 and n by 27.
So

$$h_{27} = 1 + 27 \times 6 = 163$$

Find the term with index 100 and also the one with index 1000.

(b) If we say that h_{10} of an arithmetic progression (in abbreviation A.P.) is equal to 101 and that the h_0 is 1, what is the common difference?

Formula (3) gives us

$$H = \frac{101 - 1}{10} = 10$$

(c) If we are told that in an A.P., whose common difference is 5, h_{20} is 104, what is h_0?

Formula (5) gives

$$h_0 = 104 - 20 \times 5 = 4$$

(d) What is the place of a term in an A.P. if we know that its value is 97, that h_0 is 17 and the common difference 2.

Formula (4) will give

$$n = \frac{97 - 17}{2} = 40$$

Make your own examples, choosing three of the four variables, and find the remaining one.

Note that only n has to be a whole number. For example

$$\tfrac{1}{2}, \tfrac{3}{4}, 1, \tfrac{5}{4}, \tfrac{3}{2}, \tfrac{7}{4}, 2, \ldots$$

is an A.P.: h_0 here is $\tfrac{1}{2}$, the common difference $\tfrac{1}{4}$, and according to the value of n the general term is either a fraction (a mixed number) or a whole number.

Similarly, in the following decreasing A.P.

$$100, 98, 96, 94, \ldots$$

the common difference equals -2, for, if we use formula (6), we can write

$$94 - 98 = 2H \quad \text{or} \quad H = -2$$

So we can have a great variety of A.P.s, and if we try to write many of them, changing the first term and the common difference in as many ways as we can, we will learn all that can be said about them. Is

$$-12, \quad -4, \quad 4, \quad 12$$

an A.P., and if so, what is the common difference?

6. You have often found in your games with the rods that the following patterns arise:

$$10 = 9+1 = 8+2 = 7+3 = 6+4 = 5+5 = 4+6 = 3+7 = 2+8 = 1+9 = 10$$

or $\quad 12 = 11+1 = 10+2 = \ldots = 7+5 = 6+6 = 5+7 = \ldots = 2+10 = 1+11 = 12$

If we separate each rectangle into two staircases, we can see that each staircase represents an A.P., whose first term is 1, and whose common difference is 1, there being 10 terms in the first example and 12 in the second. From the area of each rectangle we can find the sum of the terms in each A.P. In fact, the first example gives 10×11 sq. cm. for the area of the rectangle, and half of this gives the area of the staircase as $\dfrac{10 \times 11}{2} = 55$.

Now, $1+2+3+4+5+6+7+8+9+10$ is the sum of the first terms of the A.P. and we can write without counting
$$1+2+3+ \ldots +8+9+10=55$$
and similarly
$$1+2+3+ \ldots +9+10+11+12=\frac{12 \times 13}{2}=78$$

Instead of using 1 as the common difference, use any value you like and repeat what was done in section 3 above. If you form two identical staircases you can always make them fit together so as to form a rectangle. The area can easily be found by multiplying the two dimensions. So the sum of the terms of the A.P. will be half that answer.

Try it, using as many different staircases as you can make with your rods, and check your answers by calculating the length you would obtain by putting end-to-end the lengths of rods of your staircase.

7. If we use the notation of section 3 above we can write
$$h_0+(h_0+H)+(h_0+2H)+ \ldots +(h_0+nH)$$
for one staircase, and reversing it
$$\{h_0+nH\} + \{h_0+(n-1)H\} + \ldots +h_0$$
If we add the terms that are one above the other, it is the same as fitting the two reversed staircases to make a rectangle, and we get
$$(h_0+h_0+nH)+[h_0+H+h_0+(n-1)H]+ \ldots +$$
$$(h_0+nH+h_0)$$

or $\quad (2h_0+nH)+(2h_0+nH)+ \ldots +(2h_0+nH)$

always the same value for each bracket. Each term is equal to

$$h_0+h_n$$

and there are $n+1$ such terms. So for the rectangle we find the area $(n+1)\times(h_0+h_n)$ sq. cm.

So for the staircase the sum, which we shall write S, is half the rectangle:

$$(7) \quad S=\frac{n+1}{2}\,(h_0+h_n)$$

Check this formula on all the examples you have met or which you can now make.

It is clear that (7) contains again four variables: S, n, h_0 and h_n. So we can write 4 equivalent forms of (7).

$$(8) \quad \frac{2S}{n+1}=h_0+h_n$$

$$(9) \quad h_0=\frac{2S}{n+1}-h_n$$

$$(10) \quad h_n=\frac{2S}{n+1}-h_0$$

$$(11) \quad \frac{n+1}{2}=\frac{S}{h_0+h_n}$$

or $\quad (11^1) \quad n=\frac{2S}{h_0+h_n}-1$

Check whether these formulae are correct by showing that they are equivalent to (7).

Since we know by (1) that $h_n=h_0+nH$ for an A.P. we can also write (7) as

$$(7') \quad S=\frac{n+1}{2}\,[2h_0+nH].$$

54

Interesting examples

8. Each of these formulae tells you the same thing as (7). They only show how the algebra of the situation allows us to change its shape.

It follows, as in section 5, that if we give ourselves three of the four variables we can easily find the fourth one.

Let us, for example, work on the A.P. formed of odd numbers

$$1, 3, 5, 7, 9, \ldots$$

Here $h_0=1$, $H=2$ and if we use (7) we can find that for

$n=4$

$$1+3+5+7+9=\tfrac{5}{2}\times(2+4\times2)=25$$

for $n=10$

$$1+3+5+7+9+11+13+15+17+19+21=$$
$$\tfrac{11}{2}\times(2+10\times2)=121$$

In the general case

$$1+3+5+ \ldots +(2n+1)=\frac{n+1}{2}\,[2+n\times2]=(n+1)^2$$

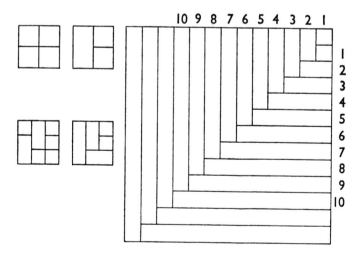

Fig. 8

55

This you can prove to yourself with the rods. Place a white rod on your table and around it 3 white ones to form a square 2×2. Replace, as in figure 8, two of the whites by a red. You can go on putting rods around and form two staircases. For example, form $1+2+3+4+5+6+7+8+9+10$ and $1+2+3+4+5+6+7+8+9$; you can make a square with them. If you start with the white and form squares as above, you can write in succession

$$1$$
$$1+(1+2)$$
$$1+(1+2)+(2+3)$$
$$1+(1+2)+(2+3)+(3+4)$$

or

$$1;$$
$$1+3;$$
$$1+3+5;$$
$$1+3+5+7; \ldots$$

whose values are

$$1, 2^2, 3^2, 4^2, \ldots$$

up to 10^2 for $1+3+5+7+9+11+13+15+17+19$. This method was already used by Pythagoras over 2500 years ago. Since

$$3=4-1=2\times2-1$$
$$5=6-1=2\times3-1$$
$$7=8-1=2\times4-1$$

and

$$19=20-1=2\times10-1$$

we find that if we go on up to the odd number 99, (which can be written

$$99=100-1=2\times50-1),$$

then the sum of

$$1+3+5+7+9+ \ldots +99$$

will be equal to 50^2 or 2,500.

Find the sum of the odd numbers up to 73, 81, 101, 455 and 999.

9. Can we do the same for even numbers?

$$2+4=6 \qquad 2+4+6=12 \qquad 2+4+6+8=20.$$

Use your rods, starting with a red one and bordering it as we did in figure 4. You get two staircases $2+3+4+5+\ldots$

$$1+2+3+4+\ldots$$

Both are the same series, but the first starts with 2. We can write in succession, as above,

2

$2+(1+3)$ using 2 terms of one A.P. and 1 of the other

$2+(1+3)+(2+4)$ using 3 terms of one A.P. and 2 of the other

$2+(1+3)+(2+4)+(3+5)$ using 4 terms of one A.P. and 3 of the other ...

or $\qquad 2=1\times 2 \qquad 2+4=2\times 3 \qquad 2+4+6=3\times 4$

$$2+4+6+8=4\times 5$$

as the areas of the rectangles formed.

So $\qquad 2+4+6+8+\ldots+20=10\times 11$

because we shall use 11 terms of one A.P. and 10 of the other.

So, in general

$$2+4+6+8+\ldots+2n=n\times(n+1)$$

Now

$$2=2\times 1, \quad 4=2\times 2, \quad 6=2\times 3, \ldots 2n=2\times n$$

so $\qquad 2+4+6+8+\ldots+2n=2\ [1+2+3+4+\ldots+n]$

$$=n\times(n+1)$$

Therefore

$$1+2+3+\ldots+n=\frac{n(n+1)}{2}.$$

This we could also have found from formula (7), since in

$$1+2+3+\ldots+n$$

$$h_0=1, \ H=1, \ h_{n-1}=n$$

57

as there are $n-1$ terms after 1. So we have

$$1+2+3+4+ \ldots +n=\frac{n-1+1}{2} (1+n) \text{ or } \frac{n}{2} \times (n+1)$$

10. If we repeat what we were doing with the rods, but, instead of the white of No. 8 and the red of No. 9, take each of the rods in succession and border them as above with other rods, to make rectangles, we could easily find the successive values of

$$3+5+7+ \ldots$$
$$4+6+8+ \ldots$$
$$5+7+9+ \ldots$$

from the areas of the rectangles formed.

Find the values of these sums by this method and check your answers using formula (7). If we note that in the first of these series $3+5=2\times4$, $3+5+7=3\times5$, etc., we see that the first factor equals the number of terms of the sum, while the second is equal to that number plus 2, and we can write:

$$3+5+7+ \ldots +(2n-1)=(n-1)\times(n+1)$$

We shall soon see (cf. No. 11) that $(n-1)(n+1)=n^2-1$, so that the result above could have been found like this:

$$1+3+5+7+ \ldots +(2n-1)=n^2$$
and $\quad 3+5+7+ \ldots +(2n-1)=n^2-1=(n-1)\times(n+1)$

You will see that you can learn a great deal from these A.P.s by looking at your results and asking yourself whether they could have been obtained by some other method.

Powers and their algebra

11. In Book II we met $(a+b)^2$ and $(a-b)^2$. The example of No. 10 is related to a third relation between squares also met in Books II and V. We consider it again here.

Make any square with your rods and choose a smaller square. Put it on top of the first so that one corner and two sides are superimposed as in figure 9. Our problem is to find the area of the difference of the two squares.

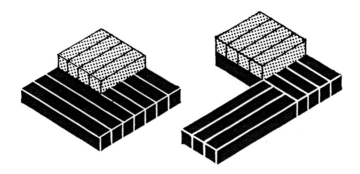

Fig. 9

It is obvious that if we turn some of the rods uncovered by the smaller square we can replace the difference of the two squares by a rectangle. Do this in the case you have chosen and find the area of the rectangle in terms of the sides of the two squares you formed.

For example, if you had chosen black and yellow squares, you have b^2-y^2 for the area equal to the difference of the two squares, and for the rectangle you have the two dimensions $b-y$ and $b+y$, so that the area of the rectangle is $(b-y)\times(b+y)$. Hence

(1) $\quad b^2-y^2=(b-y)\times(b+y)$

Test this result on any choices and consider not only the answer but what you are doing. The difference of two squares is always replaced by a rectangle whose dimensions are the sum and the difference of the sides of the squares.

In particular, $n^2-1=(n-1)\times(n+1)$ as we said above. This relation may help you to find quickly certain products if you notice a relationship. For example a difficult product such as 1025×975 can be replaced by $(1000+25)\times(1000-25)=1000^2-25^2=1,000,000-625=999,375$, obtained in no time. Instead of (1) we can also write

59

$$(2) \quad b-y=\frac{b^2-y^2}{b+y}$$

or $\quad (3) \quad b+y=\frac{b^2-y^2}{b-y}$

12.   We already know that by making towers with the rods, we can form the powers of any of the whole numbers from 2 to 10. We can easily form towers for 2^7 or 7^8 or 10^{10}. In this book we look more at what we do than at the result, so we shall use the initials of the colours of the rods instead of their length in cm. By so doing we shall find that what we do with any one colour can be repeated with all the others, so that in fact it is independent of the length.

For example, y, y^2, y^3, y^4, ... y^{20}, if we could actually form those towers, would consist of 1, 2, 3, ... 20 rods put across and on top of each other. Perhaps you can find which is the rod that gives *you* the highest tower that you can put up without too often having it fall.

With any tower you can make, you can see that you can write something like

$$y \times y = y^2$$
$$y \times y \times y = y \times y^2 = y^2 \times y = y^3$$
$$y \times y \times y \times y = y \times y^3 = y^2 \times y^2 = (y^2)^2 = y^3 \times y = y^4$$

and so on.

Form similarly all the products for higher towers up to the height you can reach.

Check the following formulae which sum up what you can find in these manipulations

$$y^m \times y^n = y^{m+n} \qquad m \text{ and } n \text{ whole numbers}$$
$$y^n \times y^n = y^{2n}$$
$$(y^n)^2 \quad = y^{2n} = (y^2)^n$$
$$y^{3n} \quad = (y^3)^n = (y^n)^3$$

and other similar ones.

60

13. We have considered every increment by one rod in our towers as a multiplication. If we start from a given tower and remove one rod at a time, we divide by its value. So

$$y^4 \div y = y^3 \qquad y^3 \div y = y^2 \qquad y^2 \div y = y$$

We must be careful not to remove the last rod, since we should find that nothing is left whereas we know that $y \div y = 1$. So we must imagine that at the bottom of the tower there is always a white rod, but actually placing it there would make our construction of the tower much more difficult.

Check the following formulae which sum up what you can find by division of powers

$$y^m \div y^n = y^{m-n} \qquad \text{if } m \text{ is greater than } n$$

$$y^{2n} \div y^n = y^n \qquad n \text{ any whole number}$$

or $\qquad \sqrt{y^{2n}} = y^n \qquad$ or $\qquad \sqrt{(y^n)^2} = y^n$

$$y^{3n} \div y^n = y^{2n} \qquad (y^{3n} \div y^n) \div y^n = y^n$$

or $\qquad \sqrt[3]{y^{3n}} = y^n \qquad$ or $\qquad \sqrt[3]{(y^n)^3} = y^n$

Geometric progression

14. If now we place another rod, say the Blue one, at the bottom of each tower and write down what happens at each stage, we have for example:

$$B, \quad B \times y, \quad B \times y^2, \quad B \times y^3, \quad B \times y^4, \quad \text{etc.}$$

This sequence is called a *Geometric Progression* or G.P.; B is its *first* term, By^n its *general* term, y the *common ratio*.

Of course we can write a large number of G.P.s by combining our rods in different ways; for example, using the red as first term and the pink as common ratio, we get:

$$r, \quad rp, \quad rp^2, \quad rp^3, \quad rp^4, \quad \text{etc.}$$

Write down a few examples that you can make. They all are towers with a bottom rod chosen to be different from the rest, not unlike the towers we had in sections 12 and 13. So we can say that powers are a special case of G.P.; namely one where the first term is equal to 1.

Of course we can vary our formations of G.P.s. For example, if instead of one rod we introduce a cross made of two rods each time, we could get the sequence

$$b \qquad by^2 \qquad by^4 \qquad by^6 \ldots$$

where the common ratio is equal to y^2.

Write the sequences corresponding to a common ratio being a "three" or a "four" made of rods of one colour.

15.   In section 14 we started with B and formed a succession of towers by placing on it a rod (or a cross or a "three" . . .) several times so as to obtain a G.P. If instead we start with a high tower we can reduce it by removing one rod (or a cross, etc.) several times. That too provides us with G.P.s. for example

$$By^N \qquad By^{N-1} \qquad By^{N-2} \ldots B$$

is a G.P. in which the terms get smaller; for this reason we shall call this a *decreasing* G.P., whereas the type of G.P. met in the previous section can be called an *increasing* G.P. In an increasing G.P. the common ratio is bigger than 1, and in a decreasing G.P. it is smaller than 1.

With numbers we can see that

8	40	200	1000	5000
$\frac{1}{8}$	$\frac{1}{4}$	$\frac{1}{2}$	1	2

are increasing, while

5000	1000	200	40	8
1	$\frac{1}{2}$	$\frac{1}{4}$	$\frac{1}{8}$	$\frac{1}{16}$

are decreasing.

In section 3 we found relationships linking the general term to the first term, the common difference and the number of terms of an A.P. It is easy to find a similar formula for the general term by^n of a G.P. If we introduce a notation using the letter t to represent the word *term* and a suffix to tell us which place it has in the G.P., we can write t_0 for the first term and t_n for the general term, and we see that

(1) $t_n = t_0 y^n$.

In this formula we have 4 quantities n, y, t_0, t_n and therefore as in No. 3 we could find 4 formulae. We shall not do so here but shall leave it for future studies because we do not yet know enough to understand all that is needed to change the relation (1) into all its forms. We can of course write

(2) $t_0 = \dfrac{t_n}{y^n}$.

but to find n will require more than we now know.

Sum of the terms of a G.P.

16. For A.P.s we used the rods to find the sum of a certain number of terms in them. In the case of G.P.s we cannot use them since our towers are only symbolic products. But in part we can calculate the sum if we make this useful observation:

$$b + by = b(1+y) = b\frac{1-y^2}{1-y} = b\frac{y^2-1}{y-1}$$

because of what we found in No. 11. Can we find formulae similar to this when we have more than two terms?

By carrying out the multiplications, we find

$$(1+y+y^2)\,(1-y) = 1-y^3$$
$$(1+y+y^2+y^3)\,(1-y) = 1-y^4$$

while

$$(1+y+y^2)\,(y-1) = y^3-1$$
$$(1+y+y^2+y^3)\,(y-1) = y^4-1$$

So

$$b+by+by^2 = b(1+y+y^2) = b\left(\frac{y^3-1}{y-1}\right) \quad \text{and}$$

$$b+by+by^2+by^3 = b(1+y+y^2+y^3) = b\left(\frac{y^4-1}{y-1}\right)$$

We shall accept that if we increase the number of terms, the formula is always of the same type and write

$$(3) \quad b+by+by^2+ \ldots +by^n=b(1+y+y^2+ \ldots +y^n)$$
$$=b\left(\frac{y^{n+1}-1}{y-1}\right)$$

This is the relation between the sum of the terms of a G.P., the first term, the common ratio, and the number of terms (which is given by $n+1$).

We can write it also like this

$$(4) \quad S_n=\frac{yt_n-t_o}{y-1}=\frac{t_o-yt_n}{1-y}$$

where S_n is the sum of the terms up to t_n.

A famous example is the sum of the grains of wheat that will be needed if we were to make a G.P. as follows: take a chess-board, on which there are $8\times8=64$ squares, and starting with 1 grain on the first square go on doubling until you reach the 64th square. We have to add

$$1+2+2^2+2^3+2^4+ \ldots +2^{63}.$$

Using formula (3) we shall have for the sum

$$\frac{2^{64}-1}{2-1}=2^{64}-1$$

In order to find out the value of this number we can see

(1) that $2^{64}=2^8\times2^8\times \ldots \times2^8$ (eight times);
(2) that $2^8=256$ and that 256 is bigger than $250=\frac{1000}{4}$
(3) that 2^{64} is bigger than $256\times256\times(\frac{1000}{4})^6$
(4) that $4^6=(4^3)^2=64^2$ and that $256\div64=4.$

hence 2^{64} is larger than $4\times4\times(10^3)^6$ or 16×10^{18}. So the sum above is larger than

$$16,000,000,000,000,000,000.$$

Can you read this number?

64

The story goes on to tell that an Indian doctor asked a rich king for that amount for having cured his beloved daughter. The king thought it was not much because he only thought of the beginning of the series. Do you think he could pay the doctor what he agreed to pay him?

17.   If successive doubling forms G.P.s, successive halving does so too. In that case the common ratio is $\frac{1}{2}$.

For example, if we start with 1 and go on halving we obtain the sequence

$$1, \quad \tfrac{1}{2}, \quad \tfrac{1}{4}, \quad \tfrac{1}{8}, \quad \tfrac{1}{16}, \quad \tfrac{1}{32}, \quad \tfrac{1}{64} \cdots$$

$$1, \frac{1}{2}, \frac{1}{2^2}, \frac{1}{2^3}, \frac{1}{2^4}, \frac{1}{2^5}, \frac{1}{2^6} \cdots$$

The sum of these fractions can be written

(5) $1 + \dfrac{1}{2} + \dfrac{1}{2^2} + \dfrac{1}{2^3} + \cdots$

and using formula (4) in its second form with $1 - y = 1 - \frac{1}{2} = \frac{1}{2}$,

$$S_n = \frac{1 - y^{n+1}}{1 - y} = 2\left(1 - \frac{1}{2^{n+1}}\right)$$

As n gets bigger and bigger, $\dfrac{1}{2^{n+1}}$ becomes smaller and

smaller, and we can say that the sum in (5) comes nearer and nearer to 2.

Application to decimal numbers

18.   What we did with the common ratio $\frac{1}{2}$ we can repeat with the common ratios $\frac{1}{10}$ or $\frac{1}{100}$ or $\frac{1}{1000}$ etc. This will help to answer a question we met at the end of Book IV, Part III. Can we find a fraction equal to any recurring decimal number?

(a)   The decimal number $\cdot33\dot{3}$ can be written as follows

$$\frac{3}{10}+\frac{3}{10^2}+\frac{3}{10^3}+\frac{3}{10^4}+\cdots=\frac{3}{10}\left[1+\frac{1}{10}+\frac{1}{10^2}+\frac{1}{10^3}+\cdots\right]$$

and this is a G.P. whose common ratio is equal to $\frac{1}{10}$.
Hence the sum of n terms equals

$$\frac{3}{10}\times\frac{1-\dfrac{1}{10^n}}{\dfrac{9}{10}}=\frac{3}{10}\times\frac{10}{9}\left[1-\frac{1}{10^n}\right]$$

As we increase the number of terms indefinitely the last bracket comes nearer and nearer to 1 and we can write for

$$\cdot 33\dot{3}=\frac{3}{10}\times\frac{10}{9}=\frac{1}{3}.$$

(b) The decimal number $\cdot 36363\dot{6}$ can be written as a G.P. with common ratio equal to $\frac{1}{100}$ since it is equal to

$$\frac{36}{100}+\frac{36}{100^2}+\frac{36}{100^3}+\cdots=\frac{36}{100}\left[1+\frac{1}{100}+\frac{1}{100^2}+\cdots\right]$$

Here again, using (4) we get

$$\frac{36}{100}\times\frac{100}{99}\left[1-\frac{1}{100^n}\right]$$

and the last bracket comes closer and closer to 1 as n increases, so that

$$\cdot 363636\ldots=\frac{36}{100}\times\frac{100}{99}=\frac{36}{99}=\frac{4}{11}.$$

(c) The decimal numbers with a *period* of more than two figures will be treated likewise except that the common ratios $\frac{1}{10}$, $\frac{1}{100}$ will be replaced by $\frac{1}{1000}$, $\frac{1}{10000}$ etc.

For example $\cdot 142857, 142857, 142857, \ldots$ with period 142857 can be written

$$\frac{142857}{10^6}+\frac{142857}{10^{12}}+\frac{142857}{10^{18}}+\cdots=\frac{142857}{10^6}\left[1+\frac{1}{10^6}+\frac{1}{10^{12}}+\cdots\right]$$

and the bracket equals

$$\frac{1,000,000}{999,999}\times\left[1-\frac{1}{10^{6n}}\right]$$

so that taking more and more terms will give for the decimal number the fraction

$$\frac{142857}{999999}=\frac{1}{7}$$

We can sum up all these cases by saying that if a decimal number is formed of a succession of the same group of figures or period, the corresponding fraction is equal to the period divided by a number formed of as many 9s as there are figures in the period.

Write down a few examples and find the corresponding fraction. Here are a few. $0\dot{3}\dot{7}$ $0\dot{7}692\dot{3}$, the dots on the successive figures linking them to form the period.

19. All the numbers we considered had no integral part. If there was one, we should only need to place it on the left of the decimal point. For example: $247\cdot\dot{3}\dot{6}$ would give us

$$247+\frac{36}{99}=\frac{247\times99+36}{99}$$

But $99=100-1$ so we can write

$$247\cdot\dot{3}\dot{6}=\frac{247(100-1)-36}{99}$$

$$=\frac{24700+36-247}{99}$$

$$=\frac{24736-247}{99}$$

If, now, the number we started with was ·247$\dot{3}\dot{6}$, having on the right of the decimal point a group of non-recurring decimals followed by a recurring group, we could observe that

$$·247\dot{3}\dot{6}=\frac{247·36}{1000}=\frac{24736-247}{99\times 1000}=\frac{24736-247}{99000}$$

So that the fraction equal to our given decimal number with an *irregular* part (247) followed by a period (36) is obtained by writing, for its numerator, the difference between the irregular part followed by the period and the irregular part, and, for its denominator, a number having as many 9s as there are figures in the period followed by as many 0s as there are figures in the irregular part.

Find the fractions equal to ·2$\dot{2}\dot{7}$, 4·70$\dot{6}\dot{9}\dot{3}$, ·90$\dot{3}\dot{7}$, by this method.

20. Later on in your studies you will meet decimal numbers that have no period or irregular part followed by a period but do not terminate. As we know that every fraction generates a periodic decimal number (with or without irregular part) and that every periodic decimal number is equal to a fraction, we can conclude that these other decimal numbers represent a new type of number. They are called *incommensurable* or *irrational* numbers.

21. Before closing this chapter let us make a remark that will help us to understand the exception to what we found in sections 18 and 19. If a decimal number is formed only of 9, and we apply our rule ·999$\dot{9}$=$\frac{9}{9}$=1 we find that ·$\dot{9}$=1. For

$$·24\dot{9} \text{ the rule gives } =\frac{249-24}{900}=\frac{225}{900}=\frac{25}{100}=·25.$$

Indeed, the difference between 1 and ·$\dot{9}$ or between ·25 and ·24$\dot{9}$ is formed of as many 0s as we write figures

$$1-·999\dot{9}=·0001 \qquad 1-·99999999=·00000001$$
$$·25-·2499=·0001 \qquad ·25-·24999999=·00000001$$

This remark will help us to write as a decimal number with an infinite number of decimals even fractions that terminate.

Give the new form of

$\cdot$35	$\cdot$76	$\cdot$81	$\cdot$93
2$\cdot$5	7$\cdot$5	8$\cdot$4	9$\cdot$7

Write the following unending decimals as decimals having a finite number of figures:

$\cdot$5299\.9   7$\cdot$99\.9   9$\cdot$\.9   99$\cdot$\.9

Find the answer to

$\frac{1}{4}-\cdot$24\.9 $\frac{3}{8}-\cdot$374\.9 $\frac{1}{2}-(\cdot$3\.9$+\cdot$09\.9$)$

V

THE GEOMETRY
OF THE GEOBOARDS

1. In the previous parts of this book we concentrated on observing the methods by which we did some of the exercises in mathematics, and we called the possibility of talking about them and using them *algebra*.

In other books of this series we learnt to use the rods in order to find properties of space. For example we learnt in Books II and VI to use the rods to obtain results concerning lengths, areas and volumes. We used them to determine the areas of squares, rectangles and of bodies formed with them. We also found how to express volumes of cuboids, prisms and bodies made of them.

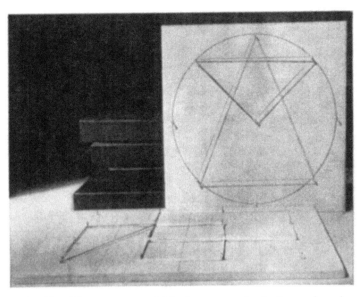

Fig. 10.   The octagon and 16-pin rectangular lattice geoboards.

In this part of the book we are going to use a new instrument, which we call a Geometry-board, or shorter, a *geoboard*. We shall obtain again some of the properties we met before, as well as many new ones. Because we shall all the time be concerned with figures and space relations, we shall call this study *geometry*.

2. You must of course have your geoboards and elastic bands every time we use them, which will be most of the time. Occasionally drawings will do.

As you can see, the geoboards are boards on which nails have been stuck in a certain pattern. When we consider the geoboards having their nails at the centres of squares as in Figure 11a, the geoboards will be said to be *rectangular lattices* (rectangular because of the right angles; lattice meaning a net or a mesh).

When we consider those which have a circle on them and nails at the centre and on the circumference as in Figure 11b, we

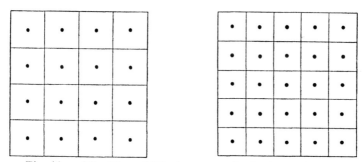

Fig. 11a.   The 16- and 25-pin rectangular lattice geoboards

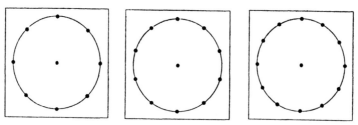

Fig. 11b.   The regular polygon geoboards

shall talk of the *regular polygon* geoboards. You have 3 of these at your disposal, the octagon, the decagon and the dodecagon. The elastic bands that go with the geoboards are of different colours so that they can be used to distinguish one line from another.

The 9–pin rectangular lattice geoboard

3.   Take the 9-pin rectangular lattice geoboard and your elastic bands. At first, use only one band. Place it on one nail and stretch it until you can join two nails. The two sides of the band now run parallel. Keeping it on one nail change the other end. How many such pairs can you find in your board?

How many of these pairs produce equal lengths?

How many different lengths between two nails do you find on your board?

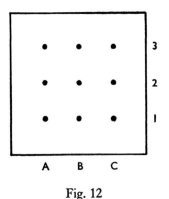

Fig. 12

In order to simplify the language, we shall give names to our nails on that board, as in the figure, and just use first a letter and then a number. For example, the bottom line or 1st line will be formed of the three nails (A,1), (B,1), (C,1). The next line or 2nd line will have the nails whose names are (A,2), (B,2), (C,2) and the next or 3rd line will be formed

72

of (A,3), (B,3), (C,3). We could have taken the nails by column and these would be the 1, 2 and 3 column.

If we join two nails, say (B,1) (A,3), we form what is called a *segment* of a *straight line*. You can see that there are as many segments on the boards as there are combinations of 2 among 9 nails, or

$$\frac{9 \times 8}{2} = 36.$$ Did you find as many as this?

We shall call *unit* length in the lattice a length equal to that of the segment from (A,1) to (A,2). Using all the necessary bands, form on your board all the segments that are there; if you can, use different colours for different lengths.

4. Start again with your board clear of elastic bands and stretch a band on three nails. You form what is called a *triangle*.

How many triangles can you form?

Fig. 13

When you choose three nails that form a segment of a straight line, as for instance (A,1), (B,1), (C,1), you will say that the three points (or nails) are *collinear*, or that the triangle has collapsed. Usually three points on one line are not considered to form a triangle. You can, of course, pull with your finger on the elastic and create a triangle with the band stretched on two nails (A,1), (C,1), for example, having (B,1) on one of its sides. Often we shall use our fingers in that way to pull on the band so that we do not think figures are only formed on nails

The triangle (B,1), (A,1), (A,2) has a *right angle* at (A,1); it is called a *right-angled triangle*. But you can find many such triangles on the board. First find those which are just like that one. Then find those which are like the triangle (C,1), (A,1), (A,2). Then again those which are exactly like the triangle (A,1), (B,2), (A,3). Where have they got the right angle? There are a few more right-angled triangles: find them.

73

Fig. 14

5.   When you look at triangle (C,2), (A,1), A,3), you see it has two sides equal. We call such triangles *isosceles* (from the Greek for equal legs). Find all the isosceles triangles there are on the board. Some of them are also right-angled. We call them *isosceles right-angled triangles*. Find all such triangles. They are of 3 sizes; do you see them?

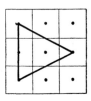

Fig. 15

6.   Triangles that have neither equal sides nor right angles are called *scalene*. For example (A,1), (A,2), (B,3) is such a triangle. Find all the scalene triangles on the board. They are of two different sizes. If you use your finger to stretch the elastic band you can make scalene triangles of any size with angles that look different.

Fig. 16

7.   Make a list of all triangles you can make on your board:
   The collapsed triangles
   The right-angled triangles
   The right-angled isosceles
   The isosceles
   The isosceles non right-angled
   The scalene

See how many of each kind you can find as we did above in Nos. 4, 5, 6.

8.   *Squares* are easily made by stretching elastic bands on four nails, as for example (A,1), (A,2), (B,2), (B,1). Find all the squares on your board made of four nails. You should find six: four equal, and two different from these and from each other.

Rectangles are also easily made. There are 4 of them. They are equal.

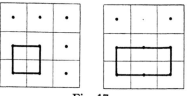

Fig. 17

Closed figures with 4 segments, called *sides*, are called *quadrilaterals*. If we reconsider squares and rectangles, we see they are quadrilaterals also.

On the board there are other quadrilaterals. For example (A,1), (A,2), (C,3), (C,2) is neither a square, nor a rectangle though it has four sides. We see that (A,1), (A,2) and (C,2), (C,3) are *parallel* and that (A,1), (C,2) and (A,2), (C,3) are also parallel. Such a quadrilateral is a *parallelogram*. There are several parallelograms on the board; find them. They are of two sizes.

Fig. 18

The quadrilateral (A,1), (C,2), (B,3), (A,2) is neither a square, nor a rectangle, nor a parallelogram. It is not given a special name; when wanting to suggest such a figure we say draw or make *any* quadrilateral. If you reconsider rectangles, do you see that they are parallelograms whose angles are right angles? If you reconsider squares, do you see that they are rectangles having all their sides equal?

Fig. 19

9. Start with (A,1), (A,2), (C,2), (C,1). It is a rectangle. Put your finger at the *vertices* (C,2) and (C,1) and move towards (B,2) and (B,1); you see that you can make rectangles, as many as you want, and while two sides are always equal to one unit, the other two sides get smaller and smaller and you pass from two units to one unit. Had you started with the square (A,1), (A,2), (B,2), (B,1) you could have stretched the band until it formed the rectangle above. This continuous

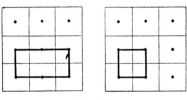

Fig. 20

movement of the vertices from (B,1), (B,2) to (C,1) (C,2), changes the square into rectangles. By continuously displacing the band you can change any figure on the board into any other. The nails pick out a few and give them a stable shape, but between any two you can form as many others as you want, if you use your fingers instead of the nails.

10. For example, start with the triangle (A,1), (A,3), (C,2). Lift the band from (C,2) and move your finger on the segment (C,2), (B,2) and then to (A,2). What can you say of all the triangles you have formed? Where is the third vertex when you move your finger so that the triangles are always isosceles?

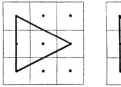

Fig. 21

11. With one elastic band you could make a figure using the four nails (A,1), (A,2), (C,2), (C,3) which is not a parallelogram. It looks like two triangles having one vertex at (B,2). Such figures are still called quadrilaterals, but with a crossing of sides or better with a *double-point*. Here (B,2) obviously belongs to the two sides (C,2), (A,2) and (C,3), (A,1).

Fig. 22

If you place the band on (C,1), (B,2), (A,1), (B,3) to form a quadrilateral, you see that it looks different from the figures

76

we had before. If you place another band along (A,1), (B,2) and stretch it you see that it cuts the side (C,1), (B,3). Similarly, if you placed another band along (C,1), (B,2) and stretched it, it would cut the side (A,1), (B,3). When this happens for some sides, the figure is said to be *concave*. When it cannot happen it is called *convex*. Verify that squares, rectangles, parallelograms, triangles are convex figures.

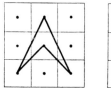

Fig. 23

12. Let us consider any of the quadrilaterals you can make on the board. There are four vertices on it. Some of them are already joined and they form the sides. If, with new coloured bands, you join vertices otherwise than along the sides, you form what is called a *diagonal* of the quadrilateral.

Fig. 24

How many diagonals are there in a quadrilateral? How many in a triangle?

Fig. 25

77

What could you say of the diagonals of the parallelograms?
What could you say of those of the rectangles?
What could you say of those of the squares?
Join (A,1), (C,1), (B,3), (A,2). You obtain a quadrilateral you
have met before. Can you say anything special about the
diagonals of that quadrilateral? Now start with the two
segments (C,1), (A,2) and (A,1), (B,3). Can you say anything
about them? With a band you can form a quadrilateral whose
diagonals are these two lines. So equality of the diagonals
and the fact that they meet at right angles do not make the
quadrilateral special.

  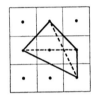

Fig. 26

Is the quadrilateral (C,1), (C,2), (B,3), (A,2) special and
are its diagonals equal, or do they meet at right angles?

13. But if we start with two lines that cut
each other in half then we always get a
parallelogram by placing another band on the
four vertices.

Fig. 27a

Try: (C,2), (A,2); (A,1), (C,3)
(B,2), (A,2); (A,1), (B,3)
(C,2), (A,3); (B,2), (B,3)

Then choose the pairs of nails to give you
equal lengths and segments that cross as, for
example, (C,2), (A,3); (A,2), (C,3), and place
a band around those four nails. What figure do
you obtain?

Fig. 27b

This property of the diagonals belongs to rectangles and we can see that any time we choose two equal lines that cut each other in half, then we always get a rectangle by joining the end points. If in addition to these properties we make the diagonals cut each other at right angles, the figure obtained by placing the band on the four nails is a square.

Try: (C,2), (A,2) and (B,1), (B,3)

(C,1), (A,3) and (A,1), (C,3)

(A,1), (B,2) and (A,2), (B,1)

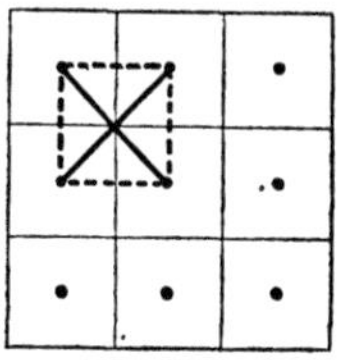

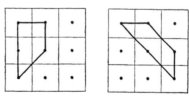

Fig. 27c

Are there other squares on the board? Can you test these properties of the diagonals on them?

14. The quadrilateral (A,1), (B,2), (B,3), (A,3) has only two sides parallel. It is called a *trapezium*. As it also has two right angles, it is called a *right-angled trapezium* or *rectangular trapezium*.

Fig. 28

The quadrilateral (C,1), (C,2), (B,3), (A,3) is also a trapezium, but as it has two sides equal it is called an *isosceles* trapezium.

Find all the trapezia there are on this board. How many are rectangular and how many isosceles? Can you say anything special about their diagonals?

15. Pulling with your finger on one vertex of a rectangular trapezium, you can form a whole family of trapezia which are neither rectangular nor isosceles.

79

But you can also keep the right angles where they are in the trapezium (C,1), (C,2), (B,2), (A,1) and move the vertex that is at (B,2). You see that you can either increase the length of the side starting at (C,2) [and at the same time diminish that of the side ending at (A,1)] until you form a rectangle and even go beyond; or diminish the length of the side ending at (C,2) until the trapezium becomes the triangle (A,1), (C,2), (C,1).

So rectangles and triangles are special cases of trapezia. Triangles are called *degenerate cases* while rectangles are called special cases.

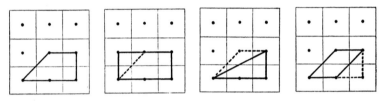

Fig. 29

Parallelograms are also special cases of trapezia, as you can prove to yourself by moving towards (B,1) the vertex that was at (C,1) in the trapezium (C,1), (C,2), (B,2), (A,1).

16. If we use 5 nails instead of four we can form a *pentagon* as for example by placing a band around (A,1), (C,1), (C,2), (B,3), (A,2). Whenever we use segments to form *closed* figures, we say we have produced a *polygon*. According to the number of the sides they are called as follows:

Fig. 30

3: triangles   4: quadrilaterals   5: pentagons,

6: hexagons,   7: heptagons,   8: octagons, etc.

Form polygons on your board and find the maximum number of nails you can use with one band. If the band does not cut itself, the polygon is either convex or concave according to the property given in No. 11. If it cuts itself it is called *stellated* and has double or triple (etc.) points according to the number of lines that go through the same point.

Start with (C,2) and join in turn to (A,3) to (B,1) to (C,3) to (A,2) to (C,1) to (B,3) to (A,1) to (C,2). The stellate octagon you obtain contains many interesting properties. Consider it and find:

Fig. 31

(a) whether the sides are equal or unequal,

(b) what the figure in the middle is,

and anything else you can notice.

17. Using as many bands as you like, you can form a great variety of polygons. If you form only one-band polygons, find how many diagonals there are in:

quadrilaterals
pentagons
hexagons
heptagons

Can you form a non-stellated octagon?

18. Let us call unit of area the area of the smallest square you can make on the nails. Find, in terms of that unit, the area of as many figures as you can form.

Here are a few examples.

Triangles (A,1), (A,2), (B,1) or (A,1), (A,2), (B,3) or (A,1), (A,2), (C,3).

Quadrilaterals: all you formed above.

Polygons: all you have formed in No. 17.

A difficult example is the crossed quadrilateral (A,1) joined to (C,3); (C,3) to (B,1); (B,1) to (B,2); (B,2) to (A,1).

Fig. 32

19. Form the rectangle (A,1), (A,2), (C,2), (C,1) and, using a band of a different colour, also form the parallelogram (A,1), (A,2), (C,3), (C,2). The area of each of these is twice the area of the triangle (A,1), (A,2), (C,2); therefore the area of the parallelogram is equal to the area of the rectangle, which is equal to 2 units.

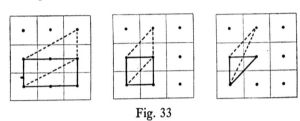

Fig. 33

Similarly we could compare the area of the square (A,1), (A,2), (B,2), (B,1) with that of the parallelogram (A,1), (A,2), (B,3), (B,2). By considering this parallelogram we can also compare the area of the triangle (A,1), (A,2), (B,2) with that of (A,1), (A,2), (B,3).

20. If we hold the board by the nail (B,2) we can make it go round and round. We say we make it *rotate* round an axis through (B,2) that stands at right angles to the board. Another way of saying 'at right angles' is to say *perpendicular* to.

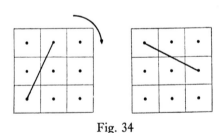

Fig. 34

Place a band so that (A,1) and (B,3) are joined. Give a rotation to the board round (B,2). You see that the line takes many positions and when it comes back to its first position, the board has turned a full turn or, as we can say, it has made a *full revolution*.

Give your board a turn equal to half a revolution. Where has the band gone?

Give it a quarter of a revolution. Where does the band finish up? Do you think we can say: the band passed from the position (A,1), (B,3) to the position (A,3), (C,2)? Place two bands on these two positions: are they perpendicular to each other?

Can you place a band on the board so that it would be in the position of (A,1), (B,3) after half a revolution? Or after three-quarters of a revolution?

21.   Instead of a line make a triangle and find where it goes after a full revolution, half a revolution, a quarter or three quarters of a revolution. Do it again with a square, a rectangle, a parallelogram.

You see that *rotation* is another way of changing a figure. Does it change size? All that is changed is the position in space. Rotation is a method of obtaining from one figure any number of figures which are in all respects equal to the first, but which are placed somewhere else in space. The figures are said to be *congruent*.

We can of course place a band on some nails and form a figure and then take the board with us, moving our body on the ground as we go along. Will the figure *on the board* change? Still, it is not at the same spot. What we did is called a *displacement* and we find that displacements do not alter a figure on the board. The original one where we first were, and the one we look at now, are not in the same spot. We shall say the figures are still congruent and that displacements produce congruent figures out of any given one.

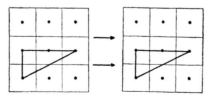

Fig. 35

If we move carefully so that the board remains parallel to itself all the time, that type of displacement is called a *translation*. So translations change a given figure into congruent ones.

22.   But we have not yet mentioned that we could rotate the board around (B,2) in two directions, which are called *clockwise* and *counter-clockwise*. In both cases the figures obtained from any one are congruent. But if we compare triangles (A,1), (A,2), (B,3) and (A,2), (A,3), (B,1)

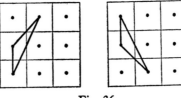

Fig. 36

we see that we cannot make them coincide by rotation (as considered in section 20) nor by translation. There is something in these two triangles that makes them look different.

Let us put one finger on side (A,1), (A,2) and another on side (A,2), (A,3) and let us move clockwise round each triangle. From (A,2) to (B,3), from (B,3) to (A,1), and from (A,1) to (A,2) on one triangle; and from (A,2) to (A,3), from (A,3) to (B,1) and from (B,1) to (A,2) on the other. Do we point at equal sides all the time? When we are on (B,3), (A,1) on one triangle we are on (A,3), (B,1) on the other, and these sides are not equal. Similarly for the next pair.

If, however, we move at a suitable speed clockwise on one and counter clockwise on the other, then at any time we are on two sides that are equal.

When this is the case we say that the figures are *orientated*, and we distinguish them by their orientation if in all other respects they are the same, as was the case with our two triangles.

84

Fig. 37a

You can see for instance that parallelograms (A,1), (A,2), (B,3), (B,2) and (A,2), (A,3), (B,2), (B,1) are also equal in all respects except orientation. The sides (A,1), (B,2) and (A,2), (B,3), though equal, cannot coincide. Trapezia (A,1), (A,2), (C,2), (B,1) and (A,2), (A,3), (B,3), (C,2) are orientated

Fig. 37b

figures equal in all other respects and cannot be made to coincide by displacement on the same plane. Squares and rectangles on the other hand, if they are equal in all respects, can be made to coincide by displacement.

Fig. 37c

A rubber band along (C,2), (B,2), (A,2) can serve as a mirror for the figures above. If one is the true object, its image is the other figure. We know by looking at ourselves in the mirror that we change left for right and vice-versa, and clockwise rotation for counter-clockwise and vice-versa. The two figures are said to be *symmetrical* with respect to the *axis* (C,2), (A,2). So when figures are symmetrical they are equal in all respects, but their orientation or *sense of rotation* is reversed.

Fig. 38

23. Let us use 4 rubber bands as follows. Triangle (B,1), (B,2), (C,2) can be made using one colour, say red. It is an isosceles right-angled triangle whose equal sides are one unit long. On these equal sides we can make two squares (B,1), (B,2), (A,2), (A,1) and (B,2), (C,2), (C,3), (B,3) using a different colour than before, say yellow. A fourth band of yet another colour, say blue, can be used to form the square (B,1), (C,2), (B,3), (A,2).

Fig. 39

In a right-angled triangle the side opposite the right angle is called the *hypotenuse*. So we now have 3 squares whose sides are respectively equal to the sides of the red triangle. If we calculate the area of the blue square we see it is equal to 4 times half a square unit, or two units; that is to say, it is equal to the sum of the area of the yellow squares. In other words: the square on the hypotenuse of this isosceles right-angled triangle is equal to twice the square on the other side. But we know that the yellow square equals one unit. So if we call h the length of the hypotenuse we find that

$$h^2 = 2.$$

Or: the length of the diagonal of the unit square is such that its square equals 2. As there is no fraction whose square equals 2, we shall write that $h = \sqrt{2}$, which we know is read 'square root of 2'. The largest square in the board has side 2

86

and its diagonal H is equal to $2\sqrt{2}$: $H=2\sqrt{2}$. The diagonal of the blue square is equal to 2, but its side equals $\sqrt{2}$.

If we make the triangle $(A,1)$, $(A,3)$, $(C,1)$, it is an isosceles right-angled triangle. The square on each of its equal sides is equal to the largest square on the board, which is equal to 4 units. The square on the hypotenuse is equal to 4 times the triangle or 8 units. So here again the square on the hypotenuse is equal to the sum of the squares on the other two sides. In particular, as H is the length of the hypotenuse we find

Fig. 40

$$H^2=8 \text{ or } H=\sqrt{8}. \text{ Thus } \sqrt{8}=2\sqrt{2}.$$

24.   If we have at our disposal a rectangular lattice of 16 or 25 or more nails, we can find that all the questions we have studied can be extended, and that many new questions can be put to us. In particular we can make many more figures than with 9 pins and can find the number of their diagonals or calculate their area. We can find that on any of the right-angled triangles that we can make, the square on the hypotenuse is equal to the sum of the squares on the other two sides. But still there are things we cannot do easily.

For example, if we try to make a triangle that has its three sides equal, or an *equilateral* triangle as it is called, we find that we cannot do it using 3 pins of the board. We can, of course, form it by moving with our finger the vertex $(C,2)$ of the isosceles triangle $(A,1)$, $(C,2)$, $(A,3)$ towards the pin $(B,2)$. Before we lift it, the side $(A,1)$, $(C,2)$ is bigger than $(A,1)$, $(A,3)$; when we move the vertex to $(B,2)$ we see that $(A,1)$, $(B,2)$ is smaller than $(A,1)$,

Fig. 41

$(A,3)$; so in between there is a position where the three sides are equal.

The regular polygon boards

25.   If we use a dodecagonal geoboard, we shall find not only that we can form equilateral triangles (several of them) but also we find a new quadrilateral: the *rhombus*, that has

87

its 4 sides equal, but not necessarily at right angles (as in the square). We also find the *regular hexagon* and many other figures.

Fig. 42

Though we can find scores of figures and properties in the various geoboards, we shall have to leave most of them for you to find by playing with the boards, inserting new bands or removing some, or stretching them to see what happens to a figure when we pass continuously from one pin to another.

To conclude this section we shall select a few properties that can easily be made obvious on the polygonal geoboards.

(a) Starting from any one nail, we can join the pins two by two taking consecutive ones, or every second, third or fourth one, and going on until we come to the initial nail. We find that if the number of nails is divisible by 4 the convex regular polygons we can form are:

The octagon or two squares or four diagonals.

Fig. 43*a*

The dodecagon or two hexagons or three squares, or four equilateral triangles or 6 diagonals.

With the decagon we can form two pentagons or 5 diagonals. We can also form stellated polygons. The

88

Fig. 43*b*

case of the decagon is the most interesting. Use different coloured bands and you will find lovely patterns. About these patterns many questions can be put which perhaps will occur to you.

(b) Let us call *diameter* the line that goes through the centre of the circle on the board, *radius* the segment that joins the centre to any nail on the circle, *chord* any segment that joins any two nails on the circle. Prove, using the coloured bands that:

Fig. 44

The diameter equals twice the radius.

The longest chord is the diameter.

If two chords are equal, then they are at the same distance from the centre. If they are unequal, the longer is nearer the centre, and the shorter further away.

(c) Let us call *angle at the centre* any angle formed of two radii, *angle at the circumference* any angle made of two chords meeting at one point on the circle, and *arc* any portion of the periphery of the circle (or circumference).

Fig. 45

Using your coloured bands and your geoboards, prove that:

89

(i) If we extend the band that formed a diameter so that it becomes a triangle with one side on the diameter and one vertex on any nail, then the angle at the nail is a right angle. This is usually expressed as: the angle in the semi-circle is a right angle.

Fig. 46

(ii) If we form an angle at the centre, and on the same arc form an angle at the circumference, the first angle is bigger than the second. In some cases you can even see that the first angle is equal to twice the second.

(d) If we choose four nails on the circumference, we form a quadrilateral. It is called a *cyclic* quadrilateral. Can you see that in such a quadrilateral the angles that are opposite each other add up to two right angles. In the special case, when one of the diagonals is a diameter, two such angles are right angles.

Fig. 47

(e) If we place a diameter and all the chords that are perpendicular to it, we find

that each chord is divided into two equal parts,

that the two arcs it forms are also cut into two equal parts,

90

that if we form the angles at the ends of the diameter and at the centre to the ends of the chords, they too are *bisected* (cut into two equal parts) by the diameter.

Fig. 48

26.   Having played with the geoboards and the bands, we see that while the rods were very helpful to make plain some of the operations of arithmetic and algebra, they were far less helpful for the study of the properties that we could show on the geoboards.

But in their turn, geoboards have their limitations as well as their good points. So if we want to move ahead we need to forge new tools. Many exist that you will meet later on when you enter higher courses. Drawing is one of them, and it will be useful if you tried to use the geometrical instruments (compasses and ruler) to draw your own patterns that remove some of the restrictions you found in the geoboards.

For instance, looking at the dodecagonal geoboard, can you, only with the help of the pair of compasses, draw an equilateral triangle on your paper?

Fig. 49

How would you draw a square? or a regular hexagon? If you draw geometrical patterns and use crayons to colour them, you can see that much of what you found in the geoboards is true in the case of bigger or smaller figures and for any position of a nail. When this is discovered, you will know properties of space and not only of the geoboard.

Geometry, as you now see, is a world in which you will meet properties of figures that are beautiful and useful whenever you want to construct any object or build any edifice. In this book you have only made a start.

Lightning Source UK Ltd.
Milton Keynes UK
UKOW03f0825131213

222968UK00002B/7/P